Zinzan Brooke's
Competitive
Edge

Zinzan Brooke's

Competitive
Edge

A Guide to Training, Toughness
and Sports Nutrition

By Lee Parore

Celebrity Books
Sports & Personality Book Publishers

Acknowledgements

The author extends his sincere thanks to the following people and organisations for their support, their talent and their contribution, direct or indirect, to *Zinzan Brooke's Competitive Edge:*

- Zinzan Brooke and Alison Imm
- Margot Butcher (Perfect Words Ltd) for the editing and photography
- Mark Smith, Photosport and the *New Zealand Herald* for additional photography
- Jim Bedwell and Mike Kerrisk of Professional Fitness for their expertise in sports nutrition and supplementation and the use of Twinlab supplements
- Dr Michael Colgan for his groundbreaking research in the field of sports nutrition and training
- Paul Chek
- Les Mills World of Fitness, Auckland
- Nike New Zealand Ltd

©1997 Lee Parore

First published in 1997 by Celebrity Books
46a Taharoto Road, Takapuna
Auckland 10, New Zealand

Layout/design by Benefitz Graphics Ltd, Takapuna, Auckland.
Typeset by Benefitz Graphics Ltd.
Cover art by Dallas Bennett.
Front Cover Photograph by Mark Smith.
Back Cover Photograph by Margot Butcher.
Printed by Publishing Press, Auckland.
Celebrity Books is the imprint of The Celebrity Book Company Limited
PO Box 331630, Takapuna, Auckland, New Zealand.

ISBN 0-9583644-3-5

Contents

Foreword

When my trainer, Lee Parore, first talked about writing a book about sports training and nutrition, I had no hesitation in committing to the project.

In the three years that I've been training under Lee, I have felt stronger and better about myself and my rugby than ever before in my life.

I look back and can hardly believe that for years beforehand - even when I was an All Black - I knew so little about how to get the best out of myself as a sportsperson. Like all young men I *thought* I knew, of course. But I was wrong. And some of the things I had worked out for myself - such as skipping breakfast on the day of a game in case it "weighed me down" - were actually the exact opposite of what I should have been doing to achieve peak performance in my sport.

The thing is, nobody advised me on what to do or what to eat, what kinds of things I should be thinking about in my training and preparation, the best way to go about it. Having said that, no two athletes are alike and it's important to work out what works best for *you*, not the person next to you, your hero or your trainer. But first you must have the knowledge that allows you to make these decisions for yourself.

Knowledge is power, and that's what this book is all about: giving you the power to get the most out of yourself and your sport.

It's not about blinding you with science or following strict plans and my story is only one example of how one player empowered himself by getting advice and using his head. But in telling my story, I hope that it can help you in your sports career.

I talk about what's worked for me in training and the lessons I learned from 11 years as an All Black, the things that turned out to be important, the things that gave me the "x-factor". Those lessons don't just apply to All Blacks. They apply to everyone with a goal in sport, whether they're young or old, a club or elite player, whether you're into rugby or rowing, snooker or softball, waterpolo or weightlifting.

Training was never meant to be easy.

No one's going to wave a magic wand over you to make you better in sport and there's no magic formula in this book because that's not the way it works. Instead, get real, train hard - but train smart. That's the philosophy behind this book and I hope you can use it to make sure you get and stay on the right track as you chase your sports goals, rather than detouring (and occasionally derailing) as I did in my career. Because I don't want anyone, especially any rugby player of the future, to make the same mistakes I did just because they didn't know any better.

Zinzan Brooke

chapter (1)

Introduction

Why Is Training So Important

The late cartoon magnate Walt Disney was always very fond of saying, "If you can dream it, you can do it". Well, few facets of human life are as full of dreams as sport. But to turn your sports dream into reality, you need more than the sheer power of a vision.

We tend to think that people who make it in sport come from nowhere - they're special, gifted people who suddenly perform and shine. But no one takes a pill and wakes up a champion. Behind their success is always continuous hard work, discipline and attitude. There's something along the way that's made the successful person stronger, tougher. So you need to use your head, to work out a way to get there over time, in order to realise your dream. To *train*.

'Training' is a word that becomes very familiar very quickly as soon as you start playing sport. You talk about 'being in training', 'going to training'. You may be doing 'gym training' or you might have 'team training' (or 'practice') after school or work. It's something you do to get better at your sport. But have you ever sat down and thought about what 'training' is? Why do you train? What do you want to become better at? And what are you really training in these sessions?

When we think of 'training', most of us automatically think of physical training: working up a sweat, making our muscles work, practising the moves and body positions we use in our sport. But is that all sport's about?

If sport were simply about how good our physiques were, most matches would be a foregone conclusion. No, what makes sport exciting and inspiring is not only the physical ability of sportspeople - their speed, power, strength and endurance, but their ability to harness their mental strength (like concentration and relaxation) and emotional strength (like choosing to 'turn it up' when the going gets tough, rather than backing down; pulling off an incredible move or shot when they're on the brink of defeat). That's why you enjoy watching Steffi Graf psyching out her opponent in tennis - and her opponent refusing to give in when she's a set down. That's why you enjoy watching Zinzan Brooke pull off an amazing drop goal because something inside him tells him he can do it.

So the first key thing to understand about training is that no matter what sport you play, you're going to be using not only your physical ability, but your mental and emotional ability. To improve, therefore, you need to train not just your body and physical toughness, but your mind, your mental and emotional toughness.

> *TRAINING IS THE ENVIRONMENT IN WHICH YOU PRACTISE*
> *BREAKING THROUGH YOUR CURRENT LIMITS*

MENTAL AND EMOTIONAL TRAINING

There's always an emotional response working within the athlete as well as a physical one. What's more, you can train that emotional response, just as you can train your body.

Think about it. In tennis, they say that the most important part of a tennis match is between points. How does the tennis player prepare for the next point? With body language and what they're saying to themselves, their "mind talk". It's the same in a rugby match. You've won or lost a scrum just before you go into it. You have to be psyched up and ready to do it, mind on the job, positive, focused. If you're not, and the other side are, they'll smash you.

One thing I've learned working with All Blacks like Sean Fitzpatrick, Zinzan Brooke, Robin Brooke and Michael Jones is that even when they don't get something right the first time in training, they don't put themselves down, call themselves stupid. They *encourage* themselves with their self-talk to do better, saying to themselves, "C'mon Sean..." or "C'mon Rob". They know the only person who can hold them back is themself.

Here's an example of how you train emotional toughness for sport. Once I was training with All Black captain Sean Fitzpatrick. We were doing what we call six-minute gutbusters, which is a difficult running exercise designed to make you work at a high intensity and pace for a relatively long period. Fitzy would get to the end of them and be so "stuffed" that all he'd want to do was to crouch with his hands on his thighs and gasp at the air. But beforehand he'd said to me, "Don't let me sink down and put my hands on my thighs, or drop my head. Make me stand up tall and keep walking around, breathing."

Fitzy was training himself to walk tall on a football field in a test match even if he was tired and really feeling it: he knew his body language was important and he couldn't let the opposition know that he was tired.

The more ingrained the qualities you want to project on the sportsfield, the easier it is to tap into them when you want to use them or just be that way naturally on the field. In other words, training is the environment in which you develop assets like discipline, focus and concentration.

We've often admired performers like golfer Frank Nobilo or Steffi Graf in tennis, sportspeople who are so ice cool under pressure. They may have been that way since childhood, of course - but chances are they have also deliberately trained and developed that aspect of their play. So you can't think of training as just, "Let's go do some runs/ push some weight/ go for a swim/ go for a bike". You have to look at the emotional and mental aspect of the type of training you're doing as well.

Here's another example. I was on a rowing machine in the gym next to Zinzan Brooke. We were doing training on the rowing machine - he couldn't run because of a groin injury, so we were using the rowing machine and a bike in certain phases of his training to safely bring up his fitness levels while he was in rehab. He was wearing his heart rate monitor and had set goals to do with his stroke rate and power output. But when Zinny had two minutes to go until the end of his interval, he dropped his pace, turned to me and said, "Lee, I'm stuffed. I've gone."

I looked at him and said, "No Zinny, you're not gone. You only *think* you're gone. Now change your posture [he'd started to slump], change what you're saying to yourself, breathe and go."

Everything about his body language and self-talk said that he had given up. And who knows? Maybe he had "gone". But we had to find out if he really had. Zinny changed his focus, brought his shoulders up, breathed deep, started saying positive things to himself about feeling good, feeling strong, powerful - and did his best time ever.

You can see that it wasn't just physical training taking place that day, even though Zinny met (and exceeded) the physical standard he'd set for himself. It was *mental and emotional* training too. That's what you need to work with all the time. That's what makes people become the best that they can become. It's not how much weight you can push, but how good you are mentally when you're training - and your training environment is the ideal place to practise and increase that capacity. If you can develop that focus in training, then when you get onto the field to play, you'll be ready to give the best that you can. If you're giving the best you can, that's all that can be asked of you and you will have achieved your potential!

PREPARATION = PERFORMANCE

When you have all three aspects firing at once, the physical, the mental and the emotional, you achieve what we call optimal performance - the goal of all athletes.

As we progress through this book we'll look at ways of training in more detail, but at the end of the day, the better prepared you are, the better you're going to perform. If you train badly, with poor techniques, incorrect methods or at the wrong time, you can be sure you'll perform badly. So the reason training is important is because it's the main environment in which you do your preparation. It's the place you set standards for yourself, or lift your standards; the place you practise, finetune, make progress. If you train the way you intend to play, you're ultimately making life a lot better for yourself.

When we talk about mental, physical and emotional training, we're talking about training resilience, strength, flexibility and responsiveness.

Resilience is your ability to recover, to bounce back - and that's not just a physical ability. Likewise, strength isn't just how much weight you can push or how high you can jump. Same with flexibility: if you're very rigid mentally, then you're only ever going to have certain viewpoints on how to do something, and that's limiting.

Margot Butcher

Zinzan Brooke is a perfect example of someone who's very flexible physically and mentally. He's got that ability to adapt and think outside the square. In today's sports, that's very important. Particularly when you reach the elite stage of a sport, you only have a split second to make up your mind as to what you're going to do with your body. If you have only one way of doing things, you'll perhaps become very predictable, a weakness in most sports. But the more options you've trained and learned, the less predictable you are to your opponents. Zinzan has always used his imagination and tried different things in training. It's the environment where he can take a risk and try new things that he might end up using on the rugby field.

Responsiveness is how quickly you can adapt; respond to a certain situation. Strength, resilience, flexibility and responsiveness all work together. They are the four building blocks of your performance and the ideal place to construct them is in training.

Zinzan Brooke learned how to use weights properly when he began working with trainer Lee Parore. This is a "bent over row" which trains the lower back and abdominals to work together and helps pull the shoulders back.

TRAINING = SCIENCE + ART

These days we have a great advantage in that we can use the world of sports science to better understand and improve the way we train. Much international research has been done on the specific effects of various types and styles of training on sport and performance. We're literally learning more and more about the body and how sports nutrition and training actually work every day.

The fitness industry has become very technological and scientific, as you'll see if you pick up a fitness magazine and wade through all the product descriptions in its advertisements. But don't be fazed, because you don't need to be a rocket scientist to gain the benefits of scientific research - you simply need to know how to ask for and get good advice.

In this book we're not going to blitz you with science or fancy words. We're going to keep it simple, because it's the basics, common sense and sound principles that you need first. Then, if you're interested in more technological information, you can get the latest by asking a good trainer or nutritionist.

So what are the basics?

Well, we know for a fact that training has a physical benefit, makes you fitter. It improves the body's systems and functions. The heart and lungs become more efficient: the ability of the lungs to take in the body's oxygen supply is increased, while the heart becomes stronger, better able to pump it around. Training makes your muscles stronger, too - capable of producing more power for longer. If you think of your body as a car, then training makes the engine work better.

But we also know that if we rely purely on science in training, we'll only ever get so far - because training is half science and half *art*.

Both are important. Science gives you knowledge and theory, allowing you to understand how to best influence your body and its biological systems and functions. Art is how you use your imagination in applying that knowledge, to make it work for *you*. As trainers we use both art and science to design specific training for an athlete, to devise a training programme that meets the special needs of his or her sport and position in that sport (e.g. a forward or back in rugby) and takes into account the athlete's own abilities.

The message here is that simply training 'harder" is not necessarily going to result in optimal performance. Sometimes you do need to train hard - but you always need to train *smart*, to train appropriately. A lot of inappropriate training might make you feel good and look impressive to everyone watching in the gym, but will actually be detrimental to your performance - which should be the thing that matters most to you as a sportsperson.

TAKE IT FROM THE MAN HIMSELF

Now we've introduced you to some of the ideas that work in sports training. But to understand the power of these basic ideas, listen to what Zinzan Brooke has to say about the effect smart training has had on his performance in rugby:

ZINZAN BROOKE:
"I played for the All Blacks for 11 years, but I only trained smart during the last three of those years. You can't change history, but looking back, I wish I'd known more about training and nutrition earlier. I wish someone had told me.

I did go to the gym in my earlier years, but I would have done most things wrong. I'd jump on the cycle to do my warm-up, see other people using machines. It doesn't take much to work out how the machines work of course, so it was easy to copy the people next to me. But I didn't know how to use the machines to benefit me as an individual. I was different from the person next to me, after all. And I didn't understand the right techniques to use to avoid injury or the wrong effect.

As an example, when you do a bench press, you should keep the weight above chest level, but I used to sometimes drop it down and bounce it off my chest - completely wrong! But that's a subtle thing that you don't know unless someone tells you. That's where a good one-on-one trainer is worth their weight in gold.

No one ever showed me until I started working with Lee in 1994, before the World Cup, and it's amazing to think of all those years I spent not doing it properly. If I felt sore in my legs, arms and chest the day after the gym, I'd think it must be because I did all the weights properly! While that can be quite a good feeling, whether you actually got any physical benefit is another story.

I used to go once a fortnight or once a month and it was just to pamper my own mind, really. Just to say I'd been to the gym. Just to be able to say to the coach that I'd been to the gym, when he asked. Sometimes I'd go the whole year and wouldn't even do any weights, which are the basis of strength training.

If I did do weights, I'd just push the stuffing out of the things and then feel sore as hell the next day. I'd think, 'Awesome, you've done this big workout!' But all I was doing was stuffing my body. I thought I could do it because I'd seen a few pictures and watched a few people. My chest would get real sore, I'd do leg presses and squats, but

Zinny demonstrates the "front squat" - using a free weight to train his abdominals and improve his leg strength, balance and stability.

it's not about throwing around 150kg and looking around the gym and seeing who's watching you as you try to whack out as many as you can. It's trying to do things properly that are specific to your position or your sport.

I first started going when I was 21, around 1986, but I relied far more on my natural talent than hard work conditioning my body. Admittedly rugby wasn't professional then and when my brother Marty and I used to get home from work, roofing in the middle of summer, we were too shattered to go to the gym. On Tuesdays and Thursdays, practice days, we used to get home at 5.15, sleep for 15 minutes then go to Marist training at 5.45. Then Monday and Wednesday we had rep training, so when you had time off you didn't feel like *spending it in the gym. That may still be the case for a lot of players who play rugby at an amateur level, but my advice is to make time for the gym work and then to make sure you use that time effectively - especially when you're rehabbing an injury. I didn't know what I was doing and may as well not have gone, as far as the effects on my strength and power were concerned. And when you don't know what you're doing you can actually increase your vulnerability to injury.*

Even when I started training with Lee, after my partner Ali (who was an aerobics instructor at Les Mills gym) introduced us, for a while I was quite skeptical about gym training. I used to be one of those guys who says, "Stuff the gym". I was very non-committal, couldn't really see how pushing weights could make me a better rugby player than I was. But I tried it - and although I didn't notice much change in the mirror, I started feeling the results quite quickly.

Weightlifting correctly proved beneficial to me: I felt stronger and better for it, particularly in my upper body; felt better going into tackles and making big hits, more comfortable because I'd done all the weight training for it. I felt better in situations where I used to be a little hesitant. I knew that I could knock out 140kg in the gym, so when I looked at a guy on the park whom I knew was only 110kg, I felt very confident I could take him on. That's a mental toughness thing as well as a physical benefit.

Also, I didn't feel the bumps and the bruises as much in training. I could knock guys over and the next day I just felt good and on top of my game. You know, there's nothing worse than going to training or playing and waking up the next morning feeling crook, like you're hung over, and thinking, 'what the hell do I do this for?' You're always going to have bumps and bruises in a contact sport like rugby, but when you know you've given it your all in training or on the day of the game and you wake up Sunday and feel good - that's a great feeling.

So I've never been that great a fan of the gym, but I know now you've got to do it, to be able to find a balance where you can do the gym work as well as play, particularly with the amount of rugby we've had over the last few years. I found out that I couldn't take the knocks week in and week out and perform to my best if I just relied on my natural ability."

chapter ❨2❩

Understanding the Science
of Training

*T*raining for sports performance is an entirely different matter to training for 'look'. If better sports performance is your goal, simply pushing machines and weights to make your body look better won't help. In fact, it will probably weaken your body's ability to cope with the rigours of playing sport and you will get injured.

To help you understand the difference between training for sports performance and training for look, here we'll introduce you to some basic scientific principles used to improve athletic performance - and a few other interesting things you might like to consider.

GENETICS

If your aim is to achieve elite competitive performance in sport - to aim for the top - to a certain extent, you do need to choose your sport, and position in that sport, wisely. The plain fact is, certain body types/heights/shapes/weights best suit certain sports.

Fortunately there's a sport to suit all genetic types, be you a tall rugby lock or a petite gymnast. Most people find out what suits them through trial and error, but you can also get advice from coaches, physiotherapists or trainers.

Some sports, like rugby and soccer, cater for almost all body types, while others are more specific. It helps, for example, to be tall if you're a rower - height gives you extra leverage as you pull on the oars, and if you don't have that, you're at a disadvantage before the race has even started.

If you have a passion for a sport that you're not ideally suited to, there's nothing wrong with seeing how far you can take yourself if that process is going to give you satisfaction. Life's about doing what you enjoy and following your dreams, after all. But reality dictates that you're unlikely to become a champion in a sport you're not physically predisposed to, and you may be more exposed to injury. You have to weigh up what you want to achieve in your sport.

THE F.I.T.T. APPROACH TO TRAINING

F.I.T.T. is an anagram that stands for:
- Frequency - how often you train
- Intensity - how hard you train
- Time - how long you train
- Type - the type of training exercises you use.

These are the four key elements of sports training, the elements you manipulate to create better performance.

In the early stages of your training, you will work on developing overall fitness - becoming fitter, a little stronger, faster, more flexible, more coordinated. These are the basics, your preparation for more specific training for your sports performance using the F.I.T.T. approach.

How does the F.I.T.T. approach work?

Well, if you've ever been a regular runner, you'll know that after running around the block for a few weeks, it starts to feel "easier". Your body has got fitter, so it doesn't have to work so hard to reach the goal. To get further gains, therefore, you need to increase the goal, to either run around the block faster (changing the Intensity), or run around twice (changing the Time).

Setting a new baseline for yourself by upping the intensity, duration, frequency or changing the type of exercise you do means you're constantly working to new levels of fitness and performance. Your body has to adapt to a new stimulus and that's what prompts it to improve itself.

Manipulating these variables well ensures continued benefits. You will continue to gain strength, power, coordination, speed, agility, and balance towards your sports-specific target.

You also need to realise that the body adapts best when a *progressive* approach is applied to your yearly training programme. Build a foundation of good posture (which we'll discuss soon), then build strength and fitness upon it, and later work to increase specific fitness capacities required by your sport (e.g. speed, acceleration, reactivity, power, etc).

Too often athletes look for short cuts. They don't exist. The fact is that certain laws apply to human physiology and you have to respect them.

Don't try to figure it all out for yourself. It's important to get good, objective advice on how many times a week you should be training, what intensity you should train at (it's useful to find a trainer who can clearly demonstrate the concepts himself or herself), how long you should be training for and what type of exercises you should be utilising.

LOADING AND UNLOADING

Coaches and trainers use the terms "loading", "unloading" and "progressive overload".

Loading is basically intentionally placing physical stress on your body (during a training session, for example) to make it perform.

Unloading is resting. This can be 'active rest' (light exercise that helps the body to recover) or 'passive rest' (complete rest, like lying on a couch reading a magazine).

Rest facilitates "recovery", which is an essential component of training. When you rest between training, the body can repair its own structure and the central nervous system can recuperate, for example. In the process, the body ensures that it is stronger, ready to cope with the next bout of training. This is what's meant by "progressive overload": you're continually manipulating the F.I.T.T. approach to ensure continued gains in your overall fitness.

Recovery is a combination of rest (abstaining from the exercise you've just been doing) and sleep (when your growth hormones are released and the body repairs itself).

For effective recovery you must also give your body adequate water and nutrition. We'll discuss what constitutes good sports nutrition in a later chapter, but for now bear in mind that your body is continually turning itself over. We know from scientific research that it takes about a year for the body to replace 98% of its molecules. The quality of your lifestyle, the food you eat and your training habits affect the way the body reconstructs itself over that time, so that the commitment you put in over a year will continue giving you benefits over the following year. It's a progressive cycle.

There's an important fifth ingredient in recovery: laughter. Having a sense of fun in your daily training (which may be as simple as sharing a joke with your training partner) means not only will you enjoy training more, but that your body will actually release chemicals that increase your ability to recover.

So, the five keys to effectively readying yourself for your next training session are:

- Adequate rest
- A good sleep
- Plenty of water
- Good nutrition
- Laughter

The key is to get the balance right between the type and amount of training you do and adequate rest to stimulate the improvement of your performance.

HOW THE BODY ADAPTS TO TRAINING

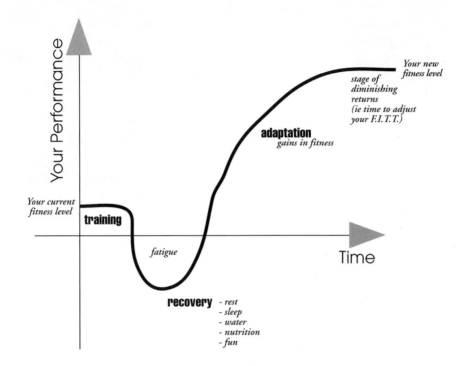

PERFORMANCE = TRAINING + RECOVERY

It's common sense that no one can train all day, every day. And you simply can't just keep making your training harder and harder, week after week - after a while the body will get tired and break down.

The above illustration shows just why you need to schedule rest in your training day - to "unload". Your body needs rest before it gives you improvement - periods of rest/recovery interspersed with periods of training. This approach should be adhered to day by day, week by week, month by month.

UNDERSTANDING YOUR HEART RATE

Monitoring your heart rate during training is important in:

• Ensuring that you're training at the right intensity and not wasting your time

• Observing and/or recording the effectiveness of your recovery

• Ensuring that you're not approaching an overtrained state.

It's important to know what we call your "maximum heart rate". To work out your maximum heart rate, we use a simple formula: just subtract your age from 220.

Next you need to know your resting heart rate. The best time to find out your resting heart rate is to take your pulse over one minute shortly after you wake up in the morning - preferably before you get out of bed.

A trainer or coach will teach you how to use knowledge of your heart rate to your advantage in training - for example, when to slow down and when to work harder. There are a number of precise formulae that you can use to work this out - it's not guesswork.

AEROBIC AND ANAEROBIC TRAINING

In most sports, much as in life, you are constantly using a combination of your body's energy and fuel systems. Your training should therefore be a combination of these as well. Basically we call the body's energy systems:

- **The Aerobic Energy System**
  This is simply when sufficient oxygen is being delivered to the working muscles. Aerobic exercise increases the body's demand for oxygen, thereby adding to the workload of the heart and lungs, raising the heart rate. It thus strengthens and develops our endurance (stamina).

- **The Anaerobic Energy System**
  This is when insufficient oxygen is being delivered to the working muscles. Anaerobic exercise of short duration activity like sprinting, weight-training, throwing, etc. will develop our power, strength and speed.

With your coach or trainer and the guidelines we give you in this book, you will be able to put together a programme that gets you fit, strong and fast, but a common mistake many young athletes make is not achieving the right balance necessary for their chosen sport. This is where your trainer or coach will be able to assist you, but you can also start by asking yourself the following questions:

- What level of stamina (endurance), strength, speed etc. do I require to perform optimally for my sport?
- How will I best achieve these - what is my plan?
- When will I know I have achieved it - how will I test myself periodically?

TRAINING FOR SPORTS PERFORMANCE

Walk into any gym and you'll see row after row of machines which you use to push or pull weight using various parts of your body. But if you only train on these machines in a gym, all you will do is train your body to perform these robotic movements.

That's not the object of anyone training for sports performance. After all, you're

Margot Butcher

Examples of training in an unstable environment:

Above left: Zinny uses both a Swiss ball and a medicine ball to train balance and stability.

Above right: Walking lunges with a medicine ball are excellent for your legs and balance.

Left: An example of three-dimensional training. This exercise trains the frontal plan with side-to-side movements.

training to become an athlete, not a robot that's good at bench presses or leg curls. Instead, you want your body to be good at functioning *three-dimensionally*. What do we mean by this? We mean that you want to be good at all three (and various combinations) of the following:

- Side-to-side movements (this is called the "frontal plane")
- Rotational, twisting movements (this is called the "transverse plane")
- Backwards or forwards movements (this is called the "saggittal plane" - the third of our "three dimensions").

Therefore, if you're training for sports performance, you need to be sure that your training methods take your body through its paces in all three of these planes (or "dimensions"). You do this by first isolating certain movements and practising them, and then combining movements in a way that you are likely to in sport.

Sport is played in what we call an "unstable environment". This is a simple way of saying that when you move in sport (and, in fact, in day to day life) your body has to constantly stabilise or balance itself. The rules aren't the same every time you move and your body has to react differently and correctly each time in order to perform at its best.

Certain training environments or techniques help your body practise this, but some don't. As an' athlete, you need to know the difference. Even a sport like snooker is played in an unstable environment: in snooker you need to be able to lean over, to balance - you need a certain amount of flexibility and strength. Think of rugby, too: when a winger is racing down the touchline, heading for the tryline, he or she might get smashed from behind by a fierce tackle. But if he or she can somehow hold their balance enough to offload the ball to a support player, points will go on the board.

You need to be training in an unstable environment that is similar and specific to your sport and its actions or movements. Your trainer or coach will guide you further in the correct exercise selection for your sport, but here are some examples:

Ways to Train in an Unstable Environment

(in all three planes)

- Use free weights
- Use Swiss balls
- Use medicine balls
- Use cable crossovers
- Use wobble boards

Ways to Train in a Stable (Fixed) Environment

(one plane only)

- Use machines

Swiss balls are like huge beach balls that you lie or kneel on while performing set exercises: because they move underneath you, they make your body work harder to stabilise and strengthen itself. Zinzan Brooke, Sean Fitzpatrick and Robin Brooke have been using the Swiss ball since October 1996 and it's become one of their key training tools.

Medicine balls are smaller and heavier, like soccer balls that weigh three to five kilos. They're used in certain exercises to make your arms or legs work a little harder to hold them or swing them through the air, at the same time making your body stabilise itself.

Exercises like these help the body develop all its "little muscles" that work together to maintain good body position when you move, twist, throw, kick, bat, run - whatever. Developing the little muscles to balance your bigger muscles keeps your body in good balance or posture, which helps prevent injuries and increase performance. The benefit of training in an unstable, three-dimensional environment is that the body has an increased capacity to stablise itself and thus more energy is available for the movements you'll use in sport (movements made with your bigger muscles but stabilised by your smaller muscles).

Training solely on machines in the gym will not help you train successfully or condition your body for the rigours of sport. However, machines do have a place in training, especially when a certain area of your body needs to be isolated (trained on its own), built up and strengthened - for example, when one area of the body is weaker than the rest because of an injury. But once you have strengthened the body part in question through the use of machines, you will still have to integrate its new strength into the movement pattern or patterns you use as a whole in sport - by training in an unstable environment instead. Machines shouldn't form the regular basis of your gym training for sports performance. You must use them wisely and at the right times.

BALANCE IN THE BODY

Another important consideration in training for sport is whether one side or the upper or lower half of your body gets used more than the other or is more dominant over the other. This might occur, for example, in tennis or squash, where a player develops a strong serve; or in rugby, where props and forwards might develop greater strength in their upper body than in their legs.

If you are constantly or regularly performing actions in your sport that particularly develop strength in one side or half of your body, over time your body will develop a physical imbalance: one side will become stronger and "tighter", while the other will be somewhat weaker in comparison. This is never desirable and it's important to analyse the specific actions you will use in sport to decide upon appropriate

Zinny uses the Swiss ball in his core training programme to develop his body's readiness for the fast-changing game of rugby.
Top: An excellent exercise for strenthening the hamstrings.
Middle: Zinny is training his lower abdominals to protect/assist/stabilise his lower back.
Above: Another example of abdominal training using the Swiss ball.

Margot Butcher

Margot Butcher

Zinny performs frontal pulldowns to help train core abdominal strength - but he uses this machine in conjunction with a Swiss ball/medicine ball/free weight programme to maximise his functional strength.

training methods that will help correct or prevent physical imbalance.

One area of the body which all athletes must pay particular attention to is the abdominals - the "core" of the body or "midsection". If you don't keep your abdominals strong, you may put your body at risk. Many people seem to believe that doing popular exercises like "sit-ups" and "crunches" are sufficient to train abdominal strength, but these exercises are not enough if you want a strong midsection or "core strength" for sports performance. To develop core strength, you need to develop and exercise a wider area, taking in your lower abdominals and part of the lower back. This is achieved by using a combination of exercises in an unstable environment - using the Swiss ball, for example, in certain ways.

This is how Zinzan Brooke felt smart, "functional" training largely in an unstable environment made a difference to him:

ZINZAN BROOKE:

"Whenever I turned up at a gym, I just used to do weights and get on the machines. I thought that was all there was to it - push and pull. There was no structure or purpose to what I was doing. I didn't understand why I did certain exercises or think whether I needed to train in different ways - and no one looked at me and said, "Well, you're a loose forward, you don't need to be quite that strong in the legs, but you do need to spend a bit more time on your upper body, because you're more of a defensive player..."

I never really felt motivated to go the gym, but looking back I think a lot of that was because I just didn't understand what I was doing. If I ever saw anything about the muscles and why we train them, it seemed like a complicated bunch of foreign words - and it didn't tell me what I needed to do specifically to make myself a better player. So I would simply go to the gym and get bored doing the same exercises every time: bench press, shoulder pull-downs, leg press and all the rest of it. I wasn't training smart - I was training dumb!

That didn't change until I started working with Lee, my trainer, a few years ago. He taught me about different muscles groups and told me why I needed to build or train some muscles in a particular way for sports strength.

When Lee showed me a Swiss ball I thought he was having me on. Then I thought he must be selling them - why else would he want me to jump on that thing? It reminded me of those toys we had as kids, the huge balls with two little "antennae" that we used to hold onto and bounce around on - I thought he wanted Zinzan Brooke and Sean Fitzpatrick to bounce around like go-go kids!

So I was very skeptical to begin with - until I actually started doing the exercises. I used to struggle like anything and only get through half the stuff. After a few weeks, my brother Robin and some of the other guys, like Michael Jones, came down to the gym and tried it, too. Michael and Rob are quite athletic guys, but when they got the Swiss ball they couldn't really do the exercises. I thought, "What's going on? These guys, when you strip them down and look at them, look like they could do anything....". But you can have a lot of muscle without necessarily being flexible, or you can be a muscly guy but with a really weak mid-section. So that was an eye-opener.

I kept up with the exercises and what I learned was that to get strong, you don't have to go and rip the hell out of the weights in your gym work. You can be a little bit more specific and intelligent about the things you do. You do have to be strong and heavy weights come into that, but you need a balance, you need to at the same time be flexible and develop this "feel" for what you're doing. I think the Swiss ball, the medicine ball and "the slide" I use are really good for that. I felt their effect especially when I was injured in my groin - I think often you don't quite understand how all your muscles work together until you have an injury like that and have to rehab it. I didn't realise how many small muscles I had around that symphosis pubis area until I had to rehab that one area - and could feel them firing, pulling on the injury when I went to do things like slide from side to side. But after time, I felt them getting better and stronger, the work getting easier.

That's what really switched me on. I realised that while we all want a nice six-pack of abs, there are muscles in the lower abdomen that you can't see the same way, but which are actually very important to your posture and ability to move. It was the same with my sciatic nerve injury: the sciatic nerve is in your back, but you can feel it in your toe! So I started to realise the mechanics of the body and how it all works together. But it's better to realise that before you learn all about it in injury and rehab.

Once I started training using the Swiss ball and these other apparati, I definitely felt stronger around my "core"; stronger in regions where I'd been lacking in the past. My groin injury actually meant that I couldn't do sit-ups or press-ups properly, or even get out of bed properly, for over a year, but through the last months of the 1997 rugby season, with the All Blacks and NPC, I could. It was hard work to get back and it took time, but the difference to my body was worth it. It's paid dividends as to how I feel today, all that hard work with the Swiss ball and medicine ball.

I think that if your body does get injured, it's a warning. You should be thinking, "Why has this happened? What's caused it?" It's just like a car: if it breaks down, there's a reason for it. There's been a cause and effect, it's not an Act of God. If you've got tight calves, you need to ask yourself why. If you pull a muscle, you have to ask yourself why. It's probably going to come down to your training and how you've gone about it, so you have to make sure you train smart."

So that's an introduction to the science of training. An athlete training for elite performance must look at balancing their training and rest, their posture (more on this soon), three-dimensional strength and fitness, and training in an unstable environment. But how do you start?

chapter ⟨3⟩

How To Start

FINDING A TRAINER

*L*ook around. Even the most physically gifted athletes in the world use a personal trainer. Basketball superman Michael Jordan, for example, has his own personal trainer, while he also trains with his team, the Chicago Bulls.

Local athletes like Michael Jones, Sean Fitzpatrick and Zinzan Brooke likewise know that the best way to begin and maintain commitment to training is to find someone who can help them manage the process and to give them a reasoned, outside perspective on their progress. You need that different perspective, someone from the outside to come and look in now and again, a qualified person who can look at the big picture with you and make sensible suggestions. If, on the other hand, you're trying to manage training by yourself, while your intentions are always good, sometimes you can lose the plot. Sometimes you're so single-minded and focused that you lose the ability to keep perspective on where you're going, what you've achieved and what you still need to do. That's the key benefit of having a personal trainer and it works for everyone from a beginner to an All Black.

Fortunately for New Zealanders we have a lot of very well trained, experienced trainers in our communities. But that helpful person doesn't necessarily have to be a personal trainer (fitness trainer). It could be a coach, a parent or a training partner.

You don't have to pick the first person that comes along. Like anything in life, finding the right solution or best formula for you is usually a little more complex than that. So set out with a plan. When you're choosing a person to help you achieve your goals, ask yourself, do they have integrity? Are they honest? What's their attitude like? What is their knowledge? Where have they learned or trained? Are they more of a

Margot Butcher

A trainer can be the eyes in the back of your head, ensuring your body's alignment is correct as you exercise - which is vital. He or she can also help you focus on and develop awareness of the muscles you're supposed to be working.

bodybuilding trainer, specialising in improving the way people look, or are they performance-orientated, sports-minded? If sports performance is your goal, choose the latter type of trainer.

Ask yourself, do I click with them? Do they understand the importance of good postural training and three-dimensional training? Have they played my sport themselves or otherwise seem to understand its requirements? Have they tried the training methods themselves? Can they demonstrate the technique they want me to use?

It's very important to feel a good rapport with the person you choose: good communication is going to help you absorb the information you need to train properly. Remember, you're going to develop a relationship with this person that will make them part of your life every week; perhaps even every day. Some of the top coaches and trainers in the world actually say it takes them five or more *years* to really train someone to the best of their ability - because it takes that long to get to know them.

It's important that your trainer or coach recognises your "training age" - that they don't give you training methods and techniques that are too advanced for your present level.

This is what Zinzan Brooke has to say about the benefits of working with a personal trainer:

ZINZAN BROOKE:
   "If you join a gym, an annual membership can be expensive, maybe $800, which is a lot of money to most people. On top of that, to get advice from a personal trainer might cost you between $30 and $60 an hour. You might not want to pay "extra" after forking out for you gym membership, but I think that's stupid. What's the point of investing in a gym membership if you don't know what you're doing in there?
   Personally I'd like to see more gyms build in complimentary personal training sessions

when you're new in a gym because it's that important to get it right. Some already do. But either way, don't think that shelling out 50 bucks for a one-on-one training session is a waste of money. It's the best investment you can make in your training. I wasted so much time in the gym because I didn't get the knowledge I needed in the first place and wasn't being monitored. Getting a trainer to at least start you off saves so many hassles. Learn it properly from the start.

I began working with a trainer in a different way to most people, because the trainer found me, rather than me seeking out the trainer. To be honest, I didn't know what was right or wrong, whether Lee's ideas were right, or right for me. I thought, I'm training with the All Blacks: what do I need this guy for? But I gave him a go because I could see he genuinely wanted to make a difference to an athlete. That was the rewarding thing for me - he thought I wasn't reaching my potential and wanted to go out of his way to make that happen.

If you don't know what one-on-one training is about, it is easy to feel a bit intimidated by it all. For young people trying to find the right person, I think it might take time. Or you might really feel comfortable training by yourself most of the time, or feel comfortable just finding a training partner. You might decide to have a one on one trainer for three or four weeks, find out some of the stuff that's specific to you and then go away with your training partner or by yourself - then get that guy back in a month's time for a training session.

It does cost you a bit of money to have a one-on-one trainer and obviously you mightn't be able to afford that. But you've always got options, you've always got a choice. You can also go to physios, coaches, managers, people - seek advice, get a general feeling about your goals, how you want to do it, how you can get help and get there. And if you're not really sure whether you've got the right trainer or whether his or her ideas are right - get a second opinion. Ask someone whose knowledge about fitness and sport you respect. I've sometimes discussed new things in training with my partner Ali, for example, because, as a dancer, she has a lot of experience in fitness and training the body and can offer me a good outside perspective.

It turned out that Lee was the right trainer for me, but he might not be the right trainer for everyone because we've all got different personalities and triggers. You've got to find a balance between you and your trainer and you've definitely got to feel comfortable in your environment - that's big. It's just like choosing a job or a bank - find one you relate to.

I can go to Lee now and say, "My body's sore, I don't really feel like this training today"; and because he relates to me he might say, "OK, we'll go do something else, let's go do some stretching or some balancing or something different."

He understands the way I feel, if I'm mentally or physically drained. Other times I might need to be kicked up the bum and he'll say, "No, you're just looking for an excuse, you're going to push through it today." We've built up a relationship where he understands how I tick and he always goes the right way."

PUT YOUR NEEDS FIRST

This is a book of practical, down to earth advice, so let's be frank. Athletes in all levels of sport often find themselves in a situation where the advice of a coach and the advice of a trainer conflicts. It may be a simple lack of communication between coach and trainer, or it may come down to a clash of ego, or a combination of both.

Whatever the reason, the important thing to remember is that everything an athlete does should be to his or her benefit - not to the benefit of the coach's, trainer's or, perhaps, parent's ego.

Ideally, where more than one person is managing an athlete's training, the coach and the trainer (or parent) should each have a good awareness of the other's input anyway. But if you're caught in an ego war, or you're getting confusing or conflicting advice, the best solution is to get all parties together and try to open a good line of communication, so that the coach and trainer can understand what each is trying to help the athlete achieve and the methods each use to reach that goal.

This may seem a daunting thing to arrange, particularly if you're a lot younger than your coach or trainer or you're still making headway in the sport. But remember, if there's no communication happening and there's a negative impact on your training as a result, who suffers? You! Don't get caught in the middle of a battle - and don't follow advice blindly.

The reality is that different people use different concepts and methods and it's likely that, as an athlete, you're going to be influenced by more than one person in your career. Of course, if you're in a team there will be times when you will have to fit in with the team's needs and this may also affect the way you train and play your sport.

TESTING AND EVALUATION: THE FIRST STEP

Once you've chosen a person to help you effectively manage your training, before you can begin to construct a training programme together you need to know two crucial things:

- What shape and condition are you really in?
- What shape and condition do you need to be in?

Next you must decide on how you are going to *test* and *monitor* yourself and your progress (i.e. the results you get from training). The following questions will assist both you and your trainer in deciding what are the most appropriate tests for you and your sport:

- Is my sport a running-based sport? If the answer is yes, then the tests you choose should be based on running (endurance or sprint, or both).
- What are the movement patterns I will use and what muscles are involved in my sport/position? You should design strength tests that specifically test them.
- Is my body in good shape to start with? What is my posture like? What do I have to do to achieve better posture (which will lead to a higher level of performance and hopefully less injuries)?
- What current, past or likely injuries are there?

A TEST IS ONLY AS GOOD AS A RETEST

Decide on when and how often you will retest yourself to monitor your progress (results). Every six to eight weeks is a good period between tests. Remember that your training should be designed to progressively improve your performance over time - it won't happen overnight (but it will happen!).

Remember the process:

Planning ➤ Training + Rest ➤ Testing ➤ Improvement

Your goalsetting (which we'll discuss further soon) should enable you to achieve results step by step - small gains often. They must be realistic goals: don't set yourself up for failure.

There is one more thing worth mentioning here. Make sure that the person testing you knows their stuff. You might be tested by a fitness trainer, sports doctor, sports physiotherapist or coach, or a combination of these, perhaps in conjunction with a sports nutritionist.

These are some of the standard scientific fitness tests currently utilised. Some of these tests may sound quite 'technical' at first, but some will soon become quite familiar to you. Ask your trainer or coach about any of these tests if you'd like to learn or understand more about how they work and what the terms mean.

1. **Testing for Maximal Aerobic Power**
   (Testing cardiorespiratory fitness, or the ability of your heart and lungs to deliver oxygen to your muscles during exercise)

   - Maximal Graded Exercise Test
     Expensive and exhausting, usually performed in a laboratory setting under the guidance of a trained individual and the most accurate method of measuring the performance of your heart and lungs.

   - The VO_2 Max Test
     This measures the same thing but indirectly, by estimating your body's maximal oxygen uptake from your heart rate during exercise. It can be wrong by as much as 10 to 20 per cent, either way.

   - Standard Distance Timed Runs
     These are straight tests of your performance, like a 3km run or 40km cycle.

2. Testing for Strength and Power

(Measured by your ability to lift weight. Remember that if your sport is largely played in an unstable environment, then these tests are best performed in an unstable environment, too)

- The Squat - how many times (repetitions) can you lift a set weight using this method of weightlifting?
- The Power Clean (as above)
- The Bench Press (as above)
- Press-ups - how many can you perform in a set time period?
- Chin-ups - how many can you do?

3. Speed / Acceleration

- Timed sprints over 5m, 10m, 40m and 100m.

4. Flexibility

- Functional Comparative Range of Motion
  (An assessment of your movement capacity around each joint - performed by a trainer or physiotherapist).
- Postural Analysis
  (An examinination of the structural alignment (balance) of your body - also performed by a trainer or physiotherapist).

5. Body Composition

(Tests can tell you how much body fat you have in comparison to lean muscle tissue, etc.)

- Bio-Electrical Impedance Analysis (BIA).
  This is the most accurate method of measuring how much body water, body fat and lean muscle tissue you have.
- Skinfold Measurements
  This uses callipers on standard sites around the body.
- Girth Measurements
  This uses a tape measure on standard sites around the body.

6. Other Tests and Considerations

- Your Blood Pressure
- Your Resting, Exercise and Recovery Heart Rate
- Medical Issues - e.g. diabetes, asthma
- Physical Disabilities - e.g. lower back pain, knee problems, etc.

Make sure you get the best advice possible in your needs analysis, usually from a good trainer or physiotherapist with experience in sports science.

POSTURAL ASSESSMENT AND TRAINING

So where are all these muscles of yours?

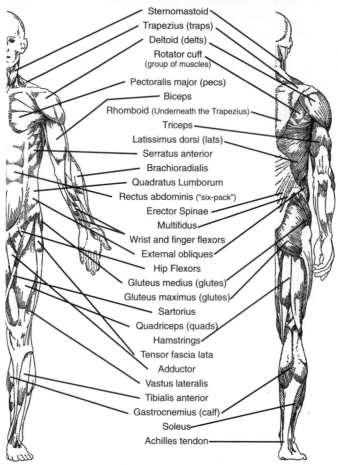

Sternomastoid
Trapezius (traps)
Deltoid (delts)
Rotator cuff
(group of muscles)
Pectoralis major (pecs)
Biceps
Rhomboid (Underneath the Trapezius)
Triceps
Latissimus dorsi (lats)
Serratus anterior
Brachioradialis
Quadratus Lumborum
Rectus abdominis ("six-pack")
Erector Spinae
Multifidus
Wrist and finger flexors
External obliques
Hip Flexors
Gluteus medius (glutes)
Gluteus maximus (glutes)
Sartorius
Quadriceps (quads)
Hamstrings
Tensor fascia lata
Adductor
Vastus lateralis
Tibialis anterior
Gastrocnemius (calf)
Soleus
Achilles tendon

Along with your specific needs analysis, the other important, vital, *crucial* thing you must do before you start any physical training programme is GET YOUR POSTURE ANALYSED AND CORRECTED.

We can't stress this enough. Good posture is the foundation of good training and good sports performance. Bad posture is the root of many preventable sports injuries and poor performance and while you may get away with it for a while, even play very well for a while with a body that you've built up in the gym by yourself without good supervision, take our word for it: you will break down - it's just a matter of time.

By good posture, we don't mean simply sitting straight up in your chair or standing tall, although this can be good posture. Good posture means that all the muscles and muscle groups in your body are in balance, working together the way they're meant to, holding various parts of your body in their right place.

Very few people turn up at a gym with their bodies completely in balance. Most of us have weaker and stronger muscle groups - and we may not even know it. What's more, as you can see in our photographs, even an athlete who would *seem* to have developed his body in the gym can actually have dangerously poor posture, exposing him to a high injury risk.

Too many young athletes don't understand that without correct supervision it's all too easy to do yourself more harm than good in a gym. Anyone can see muscle development as a result of working out - the nice-looking "mirror muscles" like the six-pack of abs, the big chest, the big thighs. But it's not so easy to see the negative effect these muscles may be having on all the little muscles in the body (like the external obliques, gluteus medius or rotator cuff you'll find by studying our 'muscle map') if you're not training the right way - the important little muscles that stabilise you during athletic performance and when you move, that create balance, create a good foundation for movement. In other words, it's all too easy to throw your body dangerously out of balance by overtraining some parts of your body in the gym and undertraining others.

For instance, how many rugby forwards have you seen with a well developed chest, but rounded, hunched shoulders, shoulders that look like they've "rolled forward"? These are players who live on the bench press in the gym. They push weights that make them feel strong in the chest and arms. But they don't realise that without doing other exercises to pull their shoulders back, as their chest and arms develop they make the shoulder girdle comparatively weak and unable to hold its natural posture. Then, when these players go to make a tackle in a game, they injure their shoulders. The tackle puts stress on the shoulder joints and the shoulder, because it has been weakened and pulled out of alignment by stronger muscles elsewhere, can't cope and "gives", breaks down.

The same applies to other parts of the body. If, for your abdominals, you concentrate only on sit-ups and crunches (to develop strong upper abs and hip flexors), you're going to create a situation where you have an excessive curve (or lordosis) in the lower spine. Your pelvis will tilt forward. Athletes who do a lot of jumping and sprinting particularly tend to get very tight in some muscles and weak in others, with this accentuated curve in the lower back, meaning they become prone to lower back pain and possible hamstring, groin and adductor problems.

The classic mistake many rugby players make is to train the upper body and not the lower body. But you've got to have balance in this sense, too - otherwise, all of a sudden you'll get knee problems, groin problems.

Some badly-trained athletes end up with such screwed-up posture that it's just a matter of time before they break down. The lack of awareness of the importance of postural analysis and training is so common that we are still seeing people at the top of their sport (like All Blacks or our cricketers) falling apart because their posture, the balance between their muscle groups, isn't good enough to hold their bodies together when they go to use them in strenuous situations on the sports field.

Think of your body as a car: even if it's a Ferrari with a nice looking chassis and good paint job, it's not going to go very well if the engine isn't working well, or if the tyres are bald or the wheels out of alignment. Drive the car fast and pretty soon it's going to break down - and you'll be stranded.

Your trainer or physiotherapist is the ace mechanic who can tell you how you're running and, most importantly, whether you should get anything fixed or finetuned before you hit the road. He or she will stop you from becoming an accident waiting to happen by analysing your posture and deciding what corrective exercises you might need to do to get your body into optimal functional balance.

If you do need to correct your posture in training, you must be dedicated, and there will be some parts of your body that you will need to constantly monitor and work on.

Basically, you will do exercises to stretch muscles that are overdeveloped and other exercises to strengthen muscles that are underdeveloped. For example, if you're one of those athletes who does a lot of jumping or sprinting with an excessive curvature of the lower back, you will work to strengthen your lower abdominal muscles, while the big hip flexor muscles at the front of your thighs will need to be stretched to correct the stress caused by the poor alignment of your spine.

Margot Butcher

This photo shows an athlete with typically poor posture through incorrect training.

You can see that he has:
- *weak muscles in the shoulder area, failing to pull his shoulders back (note the rounded shoulders)*
- *excessive curvature of the lumbar (lower) spine (this is called lordosis)*
- *weak lower abdominals*
- *tight hip flexors*
- *a lower body that is underdeveloped compared to his upper body.*

This athlete will be prone to lower back tension, possibly hamstring and adductor groin problems, and shoulder problems.

Again, it's important to realise that your postural training will only be as good as the assessment you've had done on you in the first place, and you will need to be reassessed from time to time to check your progress and improvement. Naturally, the better your posture is, the less wear and tear there will be on your body and the longer your joints will last, which means, theoretically, you should get less injuries and your sports career should last longer.

Seek out a professional who seems to you to understand the importance postural training plays in sports training. Don't guess, or try to assess it by looking in the mirror: use the training and knowledge of an expert. Too often sportspeople have bypassed this important step, thinking that because they seem strong, fit and physically gifted, they don't need to worry about the basics. Wrong. The basics are your foundation to good performance. Again, if you don't sort them out properly, sooner or later your body is going to break down - and it's probably going to be an injury you could well have avoided.

Once you can maintain muscular balance in your body, then you can look at exercises to specifically enhance your performance. Performance is actually enhanced greatly by having good posture alone, but it's enhanced further by doing your sports-specific exercises designed to give you more strength, speed, power or whatever elements or combination of elements you may be looking for specifically for your sport.

Your trainer or physiotherapist can help you put the whole training package together in the most sensible, practical way. In addition to guiding you to good posture and the right type of training programme, they will also look at your rehab issues - what kind of injuries you've had in the past, what injuries you may be carrying, what sites of your body are likely to be injured in the sport that you play. If you're a netball player, these may be ankles and knees. If you're a rugby player, it may be shoulders and lower back. If you're a rower or a cyclist, it may be lower back. The experts know and can help prevent common pitfalls.

Likewise, professionals can also assess the mental/emotional levels of a competitor (or would-be competitor), by observing how a person handles stressful situations or pressure in training situations. There are plenty of people who physically are "machines", but mentally or emotionally are babies. Plenty of athletes talk the talk, but they can't walk it. A trainer may be able to help you lift this important aspect of your game in training.

When Zinzan Brooke makes the big hits that he's renowned for in rugby, tackles where the opposition player looks like he might like to be stretchered off or have a nice, cold drink before he gets back up and keeps playing, his body has to be in good shape to be able to carry those big hits off. Zinzan's ability to tackle hard comes from not only the body position that he's been taught to tackle in, which is important, but basic posture. By practising that posture in training (and bear in mind that posture can be affected not only by physical aspects, but by your mental and emotional state - and you can practise all of these elements), when it comes to a game, his body automatically adopts good position.

These are Zinzan's own thoughts on postural training:

ZINZAN BROOKE:
"Luckily I've always pretty much looked after my posture. I've always tried to walk tall with my shoulders back and because I didn't train much in the gym when I was young I didn't fall into the trap that many young players fall into when they first see big, strong guys doing bench presses - copying them without thinking how to go about training properly.

My shoulders have rolled forward a little bit in the last couple of years, but I'm working at that now to make sure they're back and I walk tall. It's about stretching and flexibility, looking after your body, doing things properly and making sure you use all the muscles, not just some of them or the ones you can see.

It can get very scientific, but I think that it's really just about using common sense. If you do identify a problem, just make sure you do something about it, take action."

THE NEXT STEP: SETTING YOUR GOALS

All achievement in sport begins with a dream. You're inspired by other achievers in sport or by the progress you've made yourself or the enjoyment you've taken from playing. Then you begin to use your imagination to think about what's possible and create a dream picture in your mind of where you would like to be and what you would like to achieve.

You can never underestimate the sheer power of *wanting* to do something. But there are plenty of people who want to be an All Black or who want to be a top tennis player, cricketer, rower, basketballer, track and field star who haven't sat down and thought about the training stages and creative process they need to go through to develop these goals. We all want to be Superman (or Superwoman), but you've got to plan how to get there and follow that plan, rather than just dream. That's what you really must do if you are to successfully muster the commitment and drive that the best, most focused athletes use to get to the top.

Smart goalsetting is a key ingredient of effective training, no matter what your sport or level. Progressive, realistic goals provide impetus to show the dedication you need in training and, when you write them down and then meet them, create a written record of your ability to achieve things you set out to do.

The first thing you are probably going to write down is the place you want to get to: the athlete you want to be, or the level of performance you want to turn on. You may want to make a second grade team instead of a third grade team, or you may want to be good enough to win a big race that's coming up later in the year. You may want to make your school first XV, a Colts team or even the All Blacks - whatever is realistic for you as a competitor. These are examples of what we call your "outcome goal": the goal that is going to be the ultimate outcome of all your careful planning and dedicated training.

But you also need what we call "performance goals": steps along the way that will help you monitor your progress and make it to your outcome goal. When you succeed in reaching these performance goals, you will feel motivated and good about yourself in training - and your outcome or ultimate goal will be drawing closer and seem more attainable.

It's fun to write down your goals in the form of a "staircase" like this:

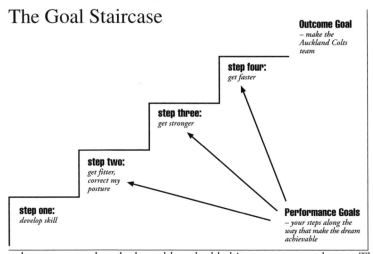

The Goal Staircase

Outcome Goal
– make the Auckland Colts team

step four:
get faster

step three:
get stronger

step two:
get fitter, correct my posture

step one:
develop skill

Performance Goals
– your steps along the way that make the dream achievable

You can also set personal goals that address bad habits you want to change. The simplest way to do this is to make two lists, like this:

What I'm doing now	What I want to do instead

You can then use these lists as a monthly checklist to remind you of your daily goals, measure how well you've responded to the challenges you've set yourself and keep yourself on target.

Here's how Zinzan Brooke addressed his daily goals - and created a checklist to keep him on track.

ZINNY'S MONTHLY PERFORMANCE CHECKLIST

WHAT I USED TO DO

Often buy a chocolate bar when I went to pay for my petrol at the gas station.

Forget about eating breakfast before training or games, or just have a cup of tea and piece of toast.

Drink Coke or Powerade when I was thirsty.

Be tempted by a cake or biscuit when I all I wanted to buy was a coffee.

Have two or three coffees.

Eat the fatty skin on chicken.

Psyche myself up intensely starting the day before a game, thinking about nothing else.

"Shut myself off" starting the day before a game and be stand-offish around other people.

Go to the gym and jump on every machine, imitating the people around me.

Do an easy session in the gym when I knew what I really needed to lift my fitness was a run.

Keep quiet about my injuries because I thought they made me seem vulnerable and also because I didn't want to give my position to someone else.

Let myself be pushed into playing when I shouldn't have played because I wasn't 100 per cent right.

Was too busy to go to physio.

WHAT I DO NOW

Eat a Powerbar between meals.

Always eat breakfast, like Porridge or Sultana Bran with trim milk (and no sugar), tea or coffee, and always drink water. Have fruit, like bananas or peaches, on my cereal instead of sugar.

Drink lots of water through the day or an Optifuel 2 shake when I know I need it. Always take a bottle of water with me.

If I need a quick bite, buy a couple of boxes of sushi, which I like and is very low-fat.

Have one coffee.

Always peel the skin off chicken - I only eat the good, white meat.

Do my mental preparation during the week, switching on and switching off.

Stay relaxed.

Use a trainer to make sure I'm doing the work that's appropriate to me and to make sure I'm doing the work sensibly and correctly.

Go for that run.

If I have an injury or I'm not 100 per cent right, take the time out and get it fixed. Do everything I can to get myself ready to go back onto the field instead of chancing it.

Ask myself if the coach has my best interests at heart and, if I'm concerned, get advice from someone who's more objective.

Make time to go to physio - fixing injuries is a priority.

KEEP A TRAINING DIARY

Once you've worked out all your goals, it's essential to keep a training diary.

Because it's the small steps along the way that lead to the big success, recognising the importance and effectiveness of those steps means you don't feel frustrated, as you might do if you only looked at the outcome goal. A diary shows you in black and white how you've achieved steps along the way - and when you're feeling down, you can use it like a tonic. You can see for yourself that you've been making steady progress over that last three weeks and the bad day you're having can quickly be put in perspective.

A training diary can be particularly helpful and inspiring when you're injured and probably feeling frustrated. Even when Zinzan Brooke was injured, he used a training diary. He said it was the little things that he wrote down and kept doing that got him back to where he was going.

During that time Zinzan had to isolate himself a little from the team, to ensure he didn't become overly competitive (because he's naturally very competitive) and as a result break himself down when he was still rehabilitating his injury. He was feeling down because he wasn't able to do what his team-mates were doing, but he kept going to the gym and out to the park to keep working on achieving little goals.

Then one day he trained with Sean Fitzpatrick. They did some shuttle runs together - and Zinzan whipped Sean's hide! (Sean may have underestimated the work Zinny had been doing - remember, never underestimate your opposition!) Suddenly Zinzan could see how much progression all the little goals had given him. That's the value of a diary: you can look back and see the benefits you've gained, the value of your training methods, the confirmation that it works. What a sense of satisfaction!

Fill in your diary the same day that you have a training session. Record what kind of weight training you have done, how many sets, how many reps (repetitions), what sort of rest periods you took, what type of stretches you did, what heart rate were you training at, what sort of fitness training you did.

The best indication of your increasing fitness is your recovery rate and it can be exciting to record the improvement. At the end of the day, it's the player or athlete who can recover the quickest who's going to be most ready to "go again", whether it be between points in a tennis match or a rugby player between lineouts and scrums or a soccer player after they've sprinted back from defence to be ready to go back on attack.

In this day and age it's possible to use technology to assist you. Sean and Zinny actually record their training sessions on high-tech watches and then download all the information from the watch straight onto a laptop computer and print it out! But pen and paper is sufficient to help you get places in training. The important thing is to be able to see and monitor what's happened in your training. You want to see how much better you're getting.

Date: **17:1:97** Body Part: **Performance Rehab** Weight: _____

Exercise	One	Two	Three	Four	Five
1 WARM-UP : Row – 6mins – distance – 1782m "Excellent Effort"					
2					
3 Front Squats	15 reps 2×60K	10 reps 1×80K	8 reps 1×90K	8 reps 1×100K	
4 Adduction Squats (Med-Ball)		10 reps 3×60K			
5 Abduction Squats (Belt)		10 reps 3×60K			
6 3-dimensional Lunges	5kg Med-Ball	3 sets			
7					
8 Standing Front Pulldowns	15 reps 1×30K	10 reps 2×40K	8 reps 1×50K		
9 Bent-Over Rows	15 reps 3×40K				
10 Swiss Ball	Press-ups 3×8	Tempo 8-1-8			
11 Swiss Ball	Hip Lifts 2×20	Side Flexion 2×10a	Forward Roll 2×10.		
12 STRETCH TO FINISH					

Diet	Other Exercise	General (Energy levels etc)

Supplements	Notes
	Workout time duration :-
	Weights — 45mins
	Swiss Ball / Abdominals — 15mins

Zinny always fills in his diary after each training session.

ZINZAN BROOKE:

"Training isn't a secret world that only some people can access. Anyone reading this book should be able to look at the words and think, 'Yeah, I can do that'. The amount of weight you bench-press, the level of your athletic ability don't determine whether you can train: it's whether you can set goals and challenge yourself to meet them. It's a process that anyone can follow.

No one's going to wave a wand over you and make you strong, after all. It takes time to train, and if you set a realistic timeframe in which to reach your goals, that makes them more achievable.

The big problem is lots of us are impatient. We turn up to the gym, look at someone who's obviously been training a long time and reached a high level of performance and think, "How on Earth am I going to get like that person?' Like, my eldest brother Naera used to come to the gym with Robin and I sometimes. We'd been going to the gym for six months consistently, but Naera would want to immediately push the same weight as us. Then he'd get despondent when he couldn't.

It would have been better if he'd started off with a lighter weight, set a goal of lifting the same weight and achieved it over three to six weeks: then he'd have the sense of getting better rather than of failing.

Everyone's different, and a 20-stone person might find it harder to achieve the same goal than a 10-stone person. But everyone can still get there if they stick to their guns. So don't get despondent.

Goalsetting definitely works. I've found that if you write down your goals and what you've done, see what you've achieved, you feel your goals are more attainable."

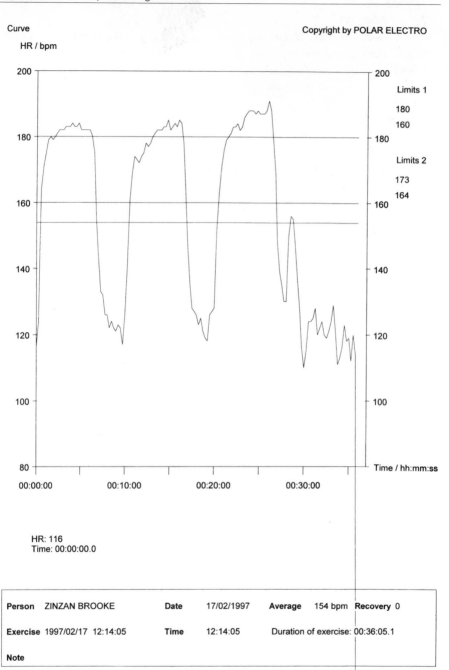

Curve

Copyright by POLAR ELECTRO

HR / bpm

Limits 1
180
160

Limits 2
173
164

Time / hh:mm:ss

HR: 116
Time: 00:00:00.0

Person	ZINZAN BROOKE	Date	17/02/1997	Average	154 bpm	Recovery 0
Exercise	1997/02/17 12:14:05	Time	12:14:05	Duration of exercise: 00:36:05.1		
Note						

The wonders of modern technology! These graphs show at a glance Zinny's heart rate, performance and recovery during different types of interval training.

Curve

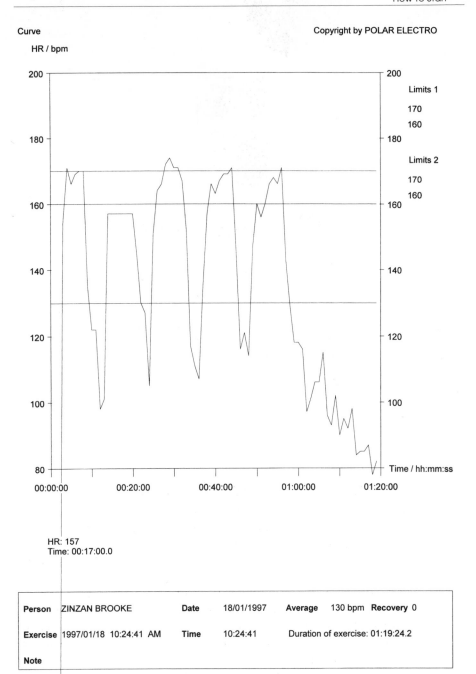

HR: 157
Time: 00:17:00.0

Person	ZINZAN BROOKE	Date	18/01/1997	Average	130 bpm	Recovery 0
Exercise	1997/01/18 10:24:41 AM	Time	10:24:41		Duration of exercise: 01:19:24.2	
Note						

chapter (4)

Planning Your Training

Y ou can't rush nature. Think of how most popular weight-loss diets work (or, more to the point, don't work): a person may lose weight while they're on it, but when they finish dieting, the weight always creeps back on. That's because most of these popular diets don't give the body enough time to recognise and adjust to its new circumstances.

Training works much the same way. You can't go on a crash course of training. Training your body for athletic performance takes time, as well as commitment. Therefore it's important to plan the way you intend to train over a set period of time - weeks, months or even over a year.

PERIODISATION: AN OVERVIEW

Planning your training over such a length of time means you must "periodise" your training, or divide it into certain periods. That's because no one can maintain top form for 12 months of the year. Even the bodies of elite athletes can't keep performing at 100 per cent every day: if they tried to, they would burn out or break down. It's simply a biological fact, a law of nature.

Think about it. How many top performers win every time they play? Look at Pete Sampras in tennis: he's a great all-round tennis player, but he doesn't win every match, every tournament he plays. So why do you automatically think of him as a top player? Because instead, he plays his best in the Grand Slam events. He tries to peak himself mentally, emotionally and physically for the ones that matter.

Tiger Woods doesn't win every tournament he plays either, but what he *does* do is often perform very well in the ones that matter. In between, he's finetuning and working to get every little thing right for the big ones. Working things out along the way, talking, trying new things, practising his putting and then putting it all together on the big day. That's the essence of what we call "periodisation" or "periodised training".

Periodisation is a system that ensures you get continued, cumulative gains from your fitness training, helps you avoid burnout and preventable injuries, and ensures you reach top form at the right time of the week, month or year.

Zinny does press-ups on a Swiss ball to create an unstable training environment.

This is how you do it. You find the date or period of the main event in your sport, whether it be a particular race (for example, an Ironman event), a major event (club finals) or playing season (the three months over which the Super 12 is played). That's called your "competition phase" or "performance phase" - the time you obviously want to be at your best.

Next, work backwards through the calendar according to how long you have to prepare for this competition phase. Think about how long you have got to get yourself in generally good shape, to improve your overall fitness and correct your posture before the competitive season for your sport kicks off. This period is divided into the "base" and the "conversion" phases.

Finally, sort out how many weeks you have where you'll be playing or performing, and which of those weeks (or games) are most important. When do you want to be playing at your best? These are the questions you must consider carefully before sitting down to work out (periodise) your training programme for the year, which is something you might like to do with your trainer or coach.

When you periodise your training programme to ensure peak performance at a critical time, break your training season into four phases. These are:

PHASE ONE   **Base Conditioning**
                   Developing your general fitness abilities, the building blocks that are going to help you achieve top form.

PHASE TWO   **The Conversion Phase**
                   The phase where you start to become a real athlete, where the intensity of your training increases and the exercises become more specific to your goal/s.

PHASE THREE **The Performance Phase**
                   Your in-season phase, the time when you need to perform, whether it's a matter of days, weeks or longer.

PHASE FOUR   **The Chill Out Phase**
                   The time for recovery (not just after your competitive season, but during all phases).

Each of these phases is important to you as an athlete and you need to manage your training according to which phase you're in at the time. So what kinds of things should you be thinking about during each phase?

PHASE 1: BASE CONDITIONING

"THIS IS THE TIME TO INVEST IN YOURSELF" - ZINZAN BROOKE

The base conditioning phase is the most important phase of your training to get right: it sets you up for your whole season. Generally it takes about 8 to 12 weeks to get a good fitness base. It's all about good preparation (such as ensuring you have got your posture right and doing exercises that will either address or help prevent the injuries your sport is most likely to expose you to). If you don't prepare well, you'll pay for it later.

Good physical (and mental/emotional) preparation is so important that some sportspeople - for example, All Blacks - may need to build two or even three base conditioning phases into their training programme over a year. It certainly wouldn't be realistic to expect one base conditioning phase to last a whole year when much of that year is spent in intense competition: physically, that's not possible.

Take the example of Zinzan Brooke in 1997. Although he'll keep working on posture and injury rehabilitation throughout the year, Zinzan built two dedicated base conditioning phases into his periodisation programme. The first was pencilled in for the 11 weeks before the season (i.e. the Super 12) began in February. The second was scheduled for after the All Black season (i.e. the Tri-Nations series) midway through the rugby year.

Although the NPC started straight after the All Blacks finished, Zinny took a couple of weeks off, and then started building up all over again in his second base conditioning phase. Doing this allowed him to spend the time he needed to fix little injuries, niggles or muscular imbalances he had picked up during All Black duty. He was preparing himself properly for his next important "competitive phase": the NPC semi-finals and the All Blacks' end of year tour to Great Britain. That was his strategy to avoid breaking down over a very long competitive season.

The overall object of the base conditioning phase is to get in touch with your body. If you're going to be an athlete, you need to get used to being in touch with things like your energy levels and feelings - like your state of fatigue. The better you are at identifying factors like these in your body, the better equipped you become to train your body and manage it so that it lasts. You know what your body can and can't handle: you know when to push, you know when to hold back in training.

One reason to keep your training as "unstable" as possible is that this type of training is far better for feeling what's happening within your body and how its working, how it's responding to and compensating for your training techniques. If, on the other hand, you're wrapped up in training on machines all the time, chances are you're not really in touch with your body that well. You may know how to push yourself; you may know how to deal with the pain barrier that all athletes must face - but that's not the same thing as really knowing your body.

These are your aims (goals) in the base conditioning phase:

- To improve your functional, three-dimensional performance capacity.

- To correct your posture.

- To rehabilitate old injuries and do your best to prevent further injury (more on this in chapter six).

- To address your weight. If you are carrying too much body fat for the performance you want, now is the time to lose it. Waiting until nearer the competitive season is simply too late.

- To get strong, working towards the maximum strength needed for your sports performance. Remember that you need to think carefully about how much strength you really need - you'll get to a point where gaining more strength will not help your performance.

- To get fit - that is, to increase your endurance. Even if your sport is primarily anaerobic, your aerobic fitness is still important, because recovery between short bursts of anaerobic activity is actually aerobic. Some of the data that the Auckland Rugby Union has collected in recent years has shown that players who make it to the top in rugby are those who have an elite aerobic fitness level, a high VO_2 Max.

- To increase your flexibility.
  Your postural assessment will show up the areas of your body that are less flexible than they need to be.

- To do some speed drills - focussing on proper sprinting technique and form.

- To improve your coordination.
  Pushing dead weight on machines won't train coordination the way free weights, medicine balls and Swiss balls will.

- To address your nutrition. This is the best time to sort out the nutrition that's going to help you get the most out of yourself. Your trainer may have a very good knowledge of sports nutrition, otherwise you can consult a sports nutritionist or dietitian, who will help educate you. If you make nutritional mistakes during your training in this phase, you still have time to learn from them, to work out the nutritional plans that really do work for you.

- To practise the way you use mind-talk or self-talk. Your self-belief can be trained just as your movement patterns can be trained. If you give yourself negative talk in training, you can expect negative performance: instead, start as you mean to continue. Maybe some negative self-talk is ingrained, something you're so used to doing or saying to yourself that you're hardly aware of it, but stop and think about it - and change those negative habits. Show yourself that you back yourself, believe in yourself.

Having considered the key areas you need to work on in the base conditioning phase, you then need to work out a training programme that will give you the results you seek, preferably with your fitness trainer or coach. To give you an idea of how a training programme can be put together, here's a sample programme that a rugby player adopted to achieve his base conditioning. (BUT NOTE! Every athlete is different. Don't just copy this programme - get expert advice to work out a personalised programme, one that's right for you and for your sport).

............................SAMPLE ONLY!............................

AIMS:
To improve posture/balance, get injuries right, improve aerobic fitness, strength, flexibility. Develop functional, three-dimensional performance capacity.

PROGRAMME:
1. Aerobic Fitness
Run an average three times a week for 45 to 60 minutes at a steady state (easy breathing) with my heart rate between 75 and 85 per cent of my maximum heart rate. I want to get fit. Other training options: cross-training like swimming, cycling and rowing, which will prevent boredom, injuries from overuse and which are types of exercise that will suit my large frame.

2. Sprint drills
Once a week, sometimes twice a week. Focus on technique and form in sprinting.

3. Strength
Train two to three times per week in the gym. Work on my posture, injuries and build up the strength I need. Include the following movement patterns to ensure I'm developing three-dimensional strength:

- Squat - 10 to 12 reps
- Lunge - 10 to 12 each side
- Deadlift - 8 to 12 reps
- Press-Ups - 20 to 50 (add resistance when necessary)
- Chin-Ups - 8-12 reps / Bent-over Rows - 12 to 15 reps
- Body Twists - 10 to 20
- Side Bends - 10 to 15 each side
- Abdominals - alternate a variety of exercises making sure I exercise both the lower region and the upper region.

Perform the above exercises for two to three sets with a rest period of one to two minutes between sets; focus on technique and a slow exercising speed. Use the right amount of weight to give me the strength I need, not more. Technique is the key. My trainer will help me get it right, but remember:
- Not to do lat pulldowns behind the head
- Shoulder presses behind the head
- Squats that lose the lower back curve
- Sit-ups with my feet anchored

(these exercises may created postural problems and increase injuries.)

4. Flexibility
Stretch every day, stretching all the major joints of my body. Use the stretching exercises I worked out with my trainer.

5. Nutrition
Eat the types of food that I worked out with my trainer and eat the right amounts at the right time before and after training. Keep my water intake steady and plentiful to help my body recover from exercise.

You'll have noticed that the player paid particular attention to training both his upper and lower abdominal muscles. That's a good example of training smart.

As we've said, most people believe (wrongly!) that sit-ups and crunches are going to do the trick as far as abdominals are concerned. But they don't really get to the muscles, the lower abs (obliques), that stabilise the midsection. It's important to recognise this, because most human movement starts with a good, strong midsection. Most of the time these popular exercises are actually going to promote *bad* posture and lower back problems.

The way to go is to train the lower abs and upper abs separately and three-dimensionally. (Train your abs with only a forward movement, like a sit-up, for example, and while the muscles might look great, you'll probably end up with an injury from twisting or sideways action in sport: you're supposed to be training movement patterns, not just muscles). Make sure you get your trainer to demonstrate techniques to build better, more functional abs. The best tools you can probably use for abdominal training are the Swiss ball and the medicine ball.

> *THE SMARTER YOUR APPROACH AND EFFORT IN THIS PHASE,*
> *THE BETTER YOU'LL PERFORM LATER*

PHASE 2: CONVERSION

You've put your body in balance and improved your fitness in your base conditioning phase. You've lost some weight, you've corrected your posture, you've sorted out your injuries and alignment, you've developed your mind-talk, your flexibility, good nutritional habits, some three-dimensional strength and stability. Now, in the conversion phase, you can start turning it up with sports-specific (performance) exercises.

We call it "conversion" because what you need to do is convert the strength you've developed as part of your base fitness into either *power* (the combination of strength and speed) that you will use on the sports field, or muscular endurance (high intensity stamina), or both.

At the same time you're also working on getting even fitter in this phase, i.e. improving your speed endurance (running faster for longer) and sharpening up your ability to sprint and accelerate.

Of course, you're after the right mix of qualities for your sport. A forward or loosie in modern rugby needs strength in the scrum, but also needs to keep up with the fast-moving running game. They will never get both the exceptional strength of a weightlifter and the endurance of a marathon runner - but that's OK. That's not what they're after - they're after the mix of those qualities that's ideal for *rugby*.

So what happens in the conversion phase?

- You concentrate on sports-specific exercises rather than overall fitness (although you are still maintaining the base you have worked up). Many of your exercises will now be in an unstable environment - because most sport is played in an unstable environment - as you look to increase your athletic ability and three-dimensional performance. Certain sports require more reactions of a certain type, and these are reactions that you can train. In netball, for example, you have to be able to grab the ball, twist, turn, and deliver the pass: that's a three-dimensional activity that can't be trained just by doing sprints. So, depending on your sport, you may now be concentrating more energy on speed training, acceleration training, or muscular endurance training.

- The intensity of your exercises becomes increasingly difficult in the conversion phase as you train what we call "functional power" for your sport. Training sessions may be shorter, but more intense. If you're working towards speed, this may be sprint training at 90 to 100 per cent maximum effort with long rest periods (from four to five minutes). If your focus is muscular endurance, your intensity is still high (anywhere from 85 to 95 per cent), but your rest periods will be shorter to encourage your body to work aerobic/anaerobically.

- You have started the sports season (you may have "friendlies", "warm-up matches" or light racing) and are now balancing training with playing. You can start "trying out" some of the abilities you have trained and build on your competitive experience. You're taking your chassis out on a few drag races to see how fast it is, see how the engine's going. It's no good, after all, keeping it wrapped up in the garage and only bringing it out on race day: you need to get to know how it's all working, and may need to finetune some features first.

- It's a good time to incorporate games into your training - fun, competitive, imaginative games that you can use to achieve results in training, either with your trainer or training partner, or in a group. You don't want to feel that you're going through the motions all the time. Training is so much more effective when you have these "releases". A sense of fun helps you "unload". Remember one of the key words of training: balance. Just as you don't want to lose perspective on your training (the big picture) or for it to become too intense, you also don't want to turn training into a joke.

- Care must be taken in this phase not to have too many hard, intense training days one after the other. Remember the body makes improvements in its peformance during periods of rest or lighter activity (easier training).

Here's how our rugby player went about converting his base fitness to sports power:

....................SAMPLE ONLY!....................

AIMS:
> To train the energy systems, movement patterns and skills I will use in rugby. To increase my functional power (strength and speed) and my muscular endurance. To get anaerobically fitter and to get faster. To keep my aerobic fitness - don't go backwards. To have fun, keep myself and my attitude "up".

PROGRAMME:
1. Anaerobic Fitness
- Higher intensity runs at 85 to 95 per cent of my maximum heart rate for 20 to 30 minutes.
- Short sprints over the distance I'll probably need in my position - 10m to 100m.

- Substitute other exercises for variety sometimes like using the rowing machine for six minute intervals (aim: 1,600m to 1,800m) or a 20 minute time trial (aim: 5,500m to 5,700m). Use my imagination to keep training fresh and stimulating. Mix it up.
- Recovery sessions every week like easy swims, cycles or runs to move the blood around my body and flush out toxins that have built up.
- Skill-training drills and games.

2. Power / Muscular Endurance

- Press-ups - increase the number, add resistance and add the plyometric (jumping) type.
- Uphill running, stair running (up the steps at the stadium), bounding.
- Medicine ball exercises performed at speed.
- Olympic-style lifts in the gym, e.g. Power cleans.
- Progress my base conditioning strength programme, possibly increasing the weights and decreasing the repetitions with longer rest periods. Focus on technique and a faster exercising speed.
- Using my imagination to vary the way I train as long as I'm training the movement patterns I want to use.
- Plyometric activities and drills - jumps, hops

3. Nutrition

- Make sure I get it right. Eat before, during and after training (using the foods and supplements I worked out with my trainer). Eat for health to help build a strong immune system.
- Make sure I eat for performance and to enhance recovery.

4. Mental

- Use positive mind-talk. It's time to push myself through limits.

PHASE 3: PERFORMANCE

As its name suggests, this phase of your periodisation coincides with the business end of your competitive season.

The key to training in your performance phase is ensuring that your body maintains its postural balance as you use it competitively. You need to be aware of your body, alert to whether one group of muscles or one side of your body is getting stronger than the other due to the overuse of those muscles when you play sport. Sports like hockey, squash, golf and tennis are often culprits here. The more attentive you are towards your posture, the less likely you will be to sustaining an injury in this phase.

Even though you're now playing at a high level of intensity, gym training still has its place in this phase because you need to maintain your strength. You may be doing

Margot Butcher

some strength work say, once every seven to 10 days, to maintain what you've built up in the base conditioning phase.

A study of NFL (gridiron) players in America showed that those who did some postural strength training and stabilisation work during the competitive season (the performance phase) had less injuries than those who didn't. So you're looking to

Another version of the press-up. This time Zinny is jumping from side to side of a medicine ball, making the exercise not only "unstable" but "plyometric" to develop explosive power in his conversion phase.

keep working on your strengths as a big match draws closer and also to keep working on your weaknesses to help keep minimise injuries.

You're also still working on sports-specific drills and exercises, perhaps for aerobic fitness, speed, reactivity or plyometrics (exercises that help you jump or spring). Medicine ball training continues to be a particularly good exercise in this phase.

You're also still working on your toughness training; the mental/emotional training you established in your base conditioning phase; and keeping up your base fitness - keep incorporating easy runs or swims into your training week. You're keeping the whole car running as smoothly as possible.

> *"THE QUICKER YOU RECOVER, THE QUICKER YOU'RE READY TO GO AGAIN" - Zinzan Brooke*

One of the most important things in your performance phase is to finetune your post-event recovery strategies. For example, if you're a runner facing a series of qualifying meets or heats in order to make a final, how effectively your body recovers between those preliminary performances will affect how well your body will be ready to perform for the next, more important race.

The day after a match or key event, it's important to do some light recovery work, to help facilitate your body's ability to repair itself. This doesn't mean going out and doing some sprint training - the key word here is "light". "Punishing" yourself with a hard training session the day after a disappointing match is a mistake. Unfortunately, many people still make it. Make sure that you're smarter than them.

Another common mistake is not going to the gym (or pool, etc) *at all* the next day. But you should actually go for a swim, or a light jog, or work up an easy sweat on the bike. Get a massage. The idea is simply to get the body moving again to speed repair and recovery.

Likewise, it's also important to manage your body sensibly as you approach an event, match, race or competition - the time you want to be in peak condition and ready to compete. This is the art of "tapering".

You don't want to leave your best performance on the training paddock, so don't have a "huge" training session in the gym, in the pool or wherever you choose to train leading up to your key event. Instead of priming your body, you'll only tire it, depleting it of energy stores and resources that it will need for the big day.

The golden rule is taper before your main event so that come race day you'll feel like you're jumping out of your skin, full of energy. Decrease the amount and intensity of your exercise as your main event approaches. Your coach or trainer will be able to give you the guidance you need to do this correctly.

So that's the performance phase. Just like base conditioning, you may need to programme in more than one performance phase per year. All Blacks, for example, have to plan for several periods of higher performance and several periods of lesser performance in order to be able to show their class over 11 months of the year.

Here's how our rugby player tackles training while he's busy playing (and team training) every week:

..........................SAMPLE ONLY!............................

AIMS:
　　To reach and maintain top form.

STRATEGIES:
- Make sure I maintain my fitness, strength and speed.
- Keep my body in balance. I will train my "main performing muscles" once a week as well as the other muscles that are on the other side of the joint to avoid injuries.
- Monitor my posture and train any weak areas.
- Implement recovery strategies. Go for an easy cycle on my exercise bike on Sunday morning, or sometimes go for an easy swim instead. Get a massage or jump into the spa most weeks. Make sure I get good rest and sleep, drink plenty of water and have fun.
- Keep thinking about my nutrition, about how I fuel my body. Keep my nutrition at an optimal level for optimal performance.
- Stretch daily.
- Stay relaxed during the week, focus as the weekend/game draws near.

PHASE 4: CHILL OUT

Elite, focused athletes like Sean Fitzpatrick, Zinzan and Robin Brooke know the importance of "chilling out" at the right times in their training and playing schedule. Being rugby's new professionals doesn't mean working intensely and devoutly 24 hours a day: it means exercising a balance that creates the best, most lasting physical and mental performance in the players. They know they shouldn't be afraid to relax now and then, to even have a couple of beers or enjoy a good wine.

The human body isn't simply a machine. It needs time out, time to repair itself, time to freshen up. The same goes for the human mind. Everyone's different, so the chill-out phase is a matter of sorting out the times and methods of "unloading" that you as an individual will respond to in order to keep you feeling fresh, healthy and happy.

If you're training seven days a week (which is extreme), you should be having "hard days" and "easy days". Likewise you will have hard weeks and easy weeks, even hard months and easy months written into your periodisation.

Better still, you should be having at least one day off a week, perhaps two. Some weeks you might feel more tired or stressed than usual: take three days off, or whatever you and your trainer thinks appropriate. Or, you might turn up to training on what's been designated a hard day, but if you're not feeling right, you can turn it into an easy day instead. You've got to listen to your body to get the most out of it, after all. Be flexible and chill out when you need to, because overtraining is good for neither your body nor your mind.

Here's the thoughts our rugby player wrote down about this very simple but important ingredient of effective training:

......................SAMPLE ONLY!......................

AIMS:
To manage my body sensibly and keep myself mentally fresh and strong.

STRATEGIES:
- To remember to vary my exercises and use fun and games in training if I'm starting to struggle with boredom.
- To take Sundays off (or have a light recovery workout). Make time to do things I enjoy like working on the house, going surfing, playing golf and catching up with friends.
- To remind myself of the word "balance" when I'm feeling frustrated after a bad game or a loss. Don't punish myself or get down, or "give up" for a while and drink too much or eat too much. Stay cool, keep on an even keel.
- Don't be too rigid or single-minded. Listen to my body and take time out when I feel really flat or tired.

So that's what periodisation is all about: the base conditioning phase, the conversion phase, the performance phase and the chill out phase. These are the basics all sportspeople will consider and work with when they sit down to plan and periodise their training season or training year in order to get the most out of their bodies and their sport.

But before we leave this chapter, listen to what Zinzan Brooke has to say about how these different phases of training really feel - and his tips on how he manages his own physical and mental wellbeing:

ZINZAN BROOKE:

"In some ways the hardest part of the season is actually before it even starts. It's when you've had the summer off, you've got sand between your toes and you're feeling like a beached whale. You look ahead to the hard yakka you know you have to do to get fitter and better and think, "How the hell am I going to get through it?"

I actually don't do it that way anymore. I find it better for me to just have six weeks off at the end of the season, and even then keep up some light maintenance work, light runs.

I worked that out last year, between 1996 and 1997. As soon as we finished the NPC in 1996, I stopped for about four weeks and turned into a couch potato. I chilled out, drunk a bit of beer, and followed the Barbarians tour with the TAB Sports Cafe. When I came back from Barbarians, I had to get stuck in again and I realised I'd probably gone the wrong way about it, that I should have kept up some maintenance work between the end of the NPC and the start of the Super 12. I ended up needing to do a truckload of work, because I had a groin injury and had to not only rehab the groin before the season started, but also build up fitness without aggravating the groin further. If you do maintenance work between seasons, it's actually easier on your body when you come back to play.

Because the seasons for top rugby players are so close together now, you don't really lose a lot of fitness. You don't get the chance! But if you play at club level, I think you have to do that little bit extra in the off-season because you finish in August and have six months' break. You've got to do work in between those seasons, and the things you can do are ball exercises and strength work.

But for us, we could actually leave the ball alone for four or five weeks, not touch it, and still come back without actually losing too much.

When I played for the All Blacks I would sit down with Lee before the start of every season and plan my whole year out. We'd get down a rough guideline and then refine it as we went. We'd look at where I wanted to be at certain times of the year. It only took half an hour to do, but it was the most important half hour I spent all year.

In 1997, there was so much rugby it was almost like playing all year. I had the Super 12, the All Blacks, the NPC and then the tour to England at the end of the year. There was no way I could have played my best every single game all year, so I had to decide what should be the pinnacles in my career and make those my focal points. I wanted to be at my peak fitness for the Super 12 finals, and then carry that form through to the end of the All Black campaign.

Then there would be a drop-off period through the NPC for a few weeks. That's when I took a couple of weeks off, because I needed to get away from rugby and slow down, freshen up. The mind actually takes longer to rejuvenate than your muscles, but it's the mind that pushes the muscles so you can't ignore it when it's fatigued.

Next I had to think about building up to hit my straps in the semi-finals and hopefully final of the NPC: that was the next main focus. We decided I should start back slowly in the early part of the NPC. As long as I did my job and we made the semi-finals, I could then aim to peak there, then drop away slightly, then go back up again for the All Black tour at the end of the year.

That completed my plan for the year, but first I had to build a solid base and that took me about 10 weeks after the Barbarians tour, from the end of Christmas to February. It's like building a house: you've got to have a solid foundation. If you don't prepare it properly, the whole house if going to be unstable and will either need repairs or fall down.

Getting your boots back on and thinking 'here we go again': that's probably one of the hardest things to get over. But after two or three disciplined weeks, once you've got into the swing of things and you start achieving little goals and you start getting better at training and you get into a routine, it's actually good.

It's amazing when you reach a peak how quickly you drop back off. That's why it can be hard starting all over again, because you know what you're capable of and you have to lift yourself back up there. Getting your weights back up there, you just grovel! But I start by pushing 60 kilos on bench press, then work a few weeks to get back up to 100, 130, 140 kilos.

I don't like power cleans at all, it's quite a hard exercise, especially when you're starting back. You can actually get your heart rate up quite quickly doing those. But I still do them, because it's important for power and strength in your glute muscles and your quad muscles.

Zinny doesn't like this exercise - the power clean - at all, but he still does it because it's important for total body strength and power.

I find that Lee helps by varying the exercises that I do. I don't want to go to the gym and think, 'God, here we go again, I did bloody bench presses last week....' Instead Lee feels when I need a rest or a change. Sometimes you can break the routine up just by doing different warm-up exercises, like doing a six-minute warm up on the rower instead of a 12 or 15 minute warm-up on the cycle. I like that, because I feel I can "compete" with the rower and if I'm only on it for six minutes, I know I haven't got long so I "blow out", feel good, then jump on the cycle for a few minutes and then hook into the weights. As long as the variety's specific to your position and your sport, variety's good. Having a trainer organise it for me also helps in that I don't know what to expect.

But while you can change things around the edges, you can't get away from the basic structure of your programme. That's important. You've still got to do bench presses to keep that strength up and shoulder work and all the rest of it. But there's other little ways you can tone up the little muscles which in turn help out the big ones.

It takes me six weeks to get a decent base, if I work hard. That's what I aim for. But as I said, I actually find it easier now to keep doing maintenance work from season to season: it's easier to do that than it is to stop cold at the end of the last match for the year or the last tour. Some people play touch over summer and that's useful - any kind of exercise is going to help. It helps mentally, too - you don't wonder what kind of shape you're in when you hit training again. It doesn't feel like such a burden. But if you just sit round like a couch potato and kick back by the barbecue all summer you'll really find it hard to come back into training in February.

Running's an important part of my base work, but to be honest, I don't like running. I can't run around an athletics track or a rugby field and find it interesting. I'd rather run through the bush or the trees, so my solution is to often run for at least 40 minutes through the Ho Chi Minh trail in the Auckland Domain, through the bush trail. I like it because it's over different terrain and you get a really good workout.

It's difficult, the first few months, especially knowing that while you're slogging away in the gym other people are out there lying in the sun. But that's just the way it is. The base conditioning phase is a little bit mentally taxing on you, but you've got to have the guts to get through it. You have to go through this pain barrier of actually doing it, because you've set yourself targets, like the time in which you're going to do certain 400m or 800m runs. Once you reach those goals and you start achieving them it does get easier.

Another thing I have to adjust is my eating habits. I get less watchful about what I eat when I'm not training, and that's OK. I feel that's the time to reward my body with some of the luxuries that I don't have all the time. I don't feel so bad about having a few bikkies and chocolates and ice-creams and maybe a few more wines or a bit more beer. But you don't go over the top. You've just got to get the right balance, make sure you have enough sweeties as well as the good stuff, but at the same time keep it in check, because it's so much harder to get it off at the other end. You want a smooth curve back, not a steep one.

Once I get my base fitness, my mind's sharper when I get out with other players and start doing good physical contact work. Mentally I'm prepared to put myself up against another player, so I don't actually find the conversion phase of my training as hard as doing all that base work.

I have a naturally competitive personality and so I really enjoy making a competition of training, trying that little bit harder to beat other players in the squad. I find it easy to start digging in a little more. You feel your body responding because it's fitter and you use your experience to know how much further you can push it each time.

Experience is the key. Like, when you're a young guy and you're full of adrenalin, all you want to do is rip the cover off everything. You've just got to be more sensible, especially when you're older. You've got to understand what your priorities are, how to pace yourself, make sure you peak at the right times, get your base and work slowly up to your peak.

Even though I had to spend longer building my base at the beginning of 1997, it was all worth it. My first game back, when I was playing the Waikato Chiefs at Albany in the Super 12 in the third week of March, I felt fine. Once I get underway, basically it's just about staying ahead of everyone else, making sure you win your games and carry on through towards peak fitness in the semis.

I kept my maintenance work going through the Super 12 - I did that the last two years, working on it all the time. It was good. It meant that when the All Black season arrived, I was better prepared mentally and physically.

Training at All Black level has always been hard physically, but sometimes in the past it was also hard mentally. It was too mentally taxing, to be honest, partly because we often didn't know what we would be doing in training, and partly because we didn't really understand the importance of having mental downtime. We didn't have the balance right between the physical and the mental aspects of our preparation.

Our first coach in the professional era, John Hart, took the mental stress out of training to a certain extent. We've still got to do some hard yakka - and hard yakka means hard yakka. But I found you gave more in the game because the mental energy hadn't been completely flogged out of you during the week. That's what took us successfully through the full-on All Black campaigns of 1996 and 1997.

I think it's good that the All Black management understand this. They don't make training a burden, which it should never be. They also gave us time out and we needed that. After a test match on a Saturday, I'd be mentally exhausted. I don't know whether young guys feel that, but for me as a senior player, I felt that because I was a major contributor to our team plans and had to take that role of nurturing the young guys through, as well as prepare and play my own game, on Saturday night after the game I'd be tired.

So on Sunday, we'd be given a day off to recharge the batteries. We'd have a team debriefing and court session for fun and that would be it. Then on the Monday we'd have a light jog - but not anything that took mental concentration or made you think, 'What's going to happen today?'. It was time out for the mind and that was good every week. You got into a regular routine that, I think, was medically beneficial to the individual and to the team. It rejuvenated us. That's one of the things that's been good about the Auckland Blues team and the Auckland team, too. It helps you through a long year.

After the All Black season, I would make it my priority to get myself patched up, to take care of my injuries and get back to the basics for a while. Sometimes you'd also get bonus weeks to do that. Like, I knocked myself out in the Super 12 final in 1997, which basically gave me two or three unexpected weeks off. I missed the All Black trial and the Fiji test, but that was maybe a blessing in disguise, a bonus. I was able to use that time to concentrate on fixing injuries and weaknesses that had built up when I was playing the Super 12.

The first few weeks of the NPC were always a little difficult because although for the All Blacks, it's the chill out phase, there's still pressure on the team to pick up early points to get a good start up the table. You also have to cope with other people's expectations - fans want you to win well. This is where you have to be responsible and just work out the right balance, the right amount of effort to make without being impatient. Because if you're impatient and want it all at once, you probably won't get to the semi-finals anyway, because you'll be laid up with injury.

In some of our games, we just knew we had the game won and so we'd just take the foot of the throttle. A classic example was our 1997 test against Australia when we were up 36-0 in the first half. People criticised our performance when we let them rack up points in the second half, but we still won the game. In fact, the only 80 minutes of rugby we've played in the last couple of years was against Australia in 1996, and no Super 12 team played an 80-minute game of rugby either in 1997. It's the nature of survival. You do what it takes to win, because when you win, you enjoy it.

The way we plan and periodise our rugby now has been very beneficial to me. It's helped me last and it's helped me enjoy what I do more.

It's a huge step forward from the way we used to train. We used to just run around the track. We had nothing to base ourselves on, no plan for the season. The key to the whole thing is that now you know what you should be doing, whereas before it was 'run around the track, do a few gutbusters, do this and do that'. We didn't understand when to do them or why we did them and it was boring as hell.

To make you more of a finely tuned athlete, it's about spending time in the gym, knowing exactly what you have to do for your position, the right technique, the reasoning behind it and how to "feel" how you're going. I've got so much more out of my training by approaching it that way and properly planning what I need to do and when I need to do it."

Zinny's Periodisation Plan For 1997

Footnote: Chill out phases to be implemented as required throughout the year.

*Base training for the 1997 season started in mid-December 1996.

chapter (5)

Warm-ups and Cool-downs

*T*his may be a short chapter, but it's a big subject. Warm-ups and cool-downs are techniques that all smart athletes must learn to use religiously in their daily training and playing life.

FIRST THINGS FIRST: THE WARM-UP

It is essential to always prepare your mind and body for the activity that is to come in any episode of training or in a game or event. By doing exercises to 'warm up', what you're actually doing is increasing your body temperature, which in turn allows greater and freer movement of your limbs. The joints and muscles find it easier to do their work. A good warm-up is therefore important in preventing injuries that you can easily avoid.

Your warm-up should include movement of the body as whole, and particularly warm up those parts of the body, muscles or movement actions that will be used in training or playing.

In general it takes 10 to 20 minutes to warm up properly. An ideal duration is one that simply leaves you feeling "warm", loose and possibly slightly sweating.

Different sports will require specific warm-up times, types and focus. But as always, it's important to still listen to your body during the warm-up phase, progressively increasing the intensity and periodically stopping to stretch - this wakes up your body, preparing it for the upcoming activity. Essentially you are switching your body on. Games that are fun, challenging and involve a skill factor are ideal.

Margot Butcher

This is Zinny's favourite stretch for his hamstrings and back.

DON'T FORGET TO COOL DOWN

Many athletes put excellent preparation in before they train or play, but in the excitement afterwards forget the important discipline of cool-downs: the simple little exercises you should do soon after any physical activity.

Cool-downs are essential. They may include some form of gentle activity to assist in the removal of waste products (toxins) from your muscles. Your focus will be stretching your muscles to return exercised muscle fibres to their normal, resting length, which will help restore postural alignment and avoid injuries in the long term.

Cool-downs also provide an ideal time to reflect upon your training session, quieten your mind, switch off and get on with the rest of your day.

These are the muscles that you will focus on stretching during both your warm-ups and cool-downs:

- Those parts of the body that are most used in the training session
- Your calf muscles (straight and bent leg stretches)
- Hip flexors and quadriceps
- Glutes (bum) and hips
- Hamstrings
- Lower back
- Pectorals (chest) and shoulders
- Neck
- Waist (midsection)
- Anywhere that you feel 'tight'.

This is what Zinzan Brooke has to say about the importance of stretching:

Margot Butcher

ZINZAN BROOKE:

"I think this is a big subject that is still very poorly understood by a lot of players. They learn plenty of techniques as far as playing the game better goes, but I think some of the fundamentals - the key ingredients, simple things like nutrition and stretching, aren't given enough emphasis. I think we get blasé about stretching especially, but it's a discipline that needs to be instilled in our kids, when we're younger, as soon as we start playing sport. Teaching kids how to stretch, how to look after themselves and eat, should be part of teaching kids the game. It's just as important as training a kid how to pass and catch a ball (skills). Those are the three key elements to getting more successful along the way. That's not just in rugby, that's in any sport.

Zinny stretching his hip flexors.

I know a lot of coaches are volunteers and a lot of them don't have the resources to go out and do anything fancy. Some of them are just parents giving up their time. But they should at least ensure kids know what they need to find out.

I would have been one of the worst ones when I started playing - I didn't understand how important proper, thoughtful stretching was at all. In Puhoi our 'stretching' was sliding round the mud for five minutes! Later it was playing 'walking touch' and then lightly jogging. That was me. I didn't understand the mechanics of the body, how it operated, that you've got to warm your body up properly. Sometimes I used to warm my body up all right, but I didn't do calf stretches and Achilles stretches or any of the specifics I really needed to.

Stretching can sound like a boring thing to do. You're usually more interested in getting out onto the paddock and seeing how high you can punt the ball than stretching your legs - but it's something you've got to be religious about. Stretching also helps your flexibility and that can help you prevent injuries. I think the perfect example of that is All Black prop Craig Dowd. Even though, to look at him, he's a big man, he's incredibly supple because he's been stretching his body properly for years and years. His sister is a ballerina and so he was influenced by her methods when he was growing up. In ballet every single muscle is warmed and stretched before you start jumping or running - and you don't see many ballerinas doing a hammie. Sport should be no different.

Craig Dowd can actually do the splits, can put his hands flat on the ground with his legs dead straight and can put his head between his legs. He's all stretched and supple - and I can't ever remember him doing a hammie or a calf."

chapter ❬ 6 ❭

Addressing
Your Injuries

*I*njury is the bane of sportspeople. Split webbings, torn hamstrings, shin splints,
muscle strains - they're painful irritations that you'd rather do without. And, of
course, if you have an injury, you have to put your sporting goals on hold sometimes,
miss games that perhaps you were really looking forward to playing, miss chances for
selection, chances of victory, even miss entire seasons.

Naturally, then, as an athlete you want to take responsibility and do everything
you can do to (a) prevent injury and (b) if you have an injury, to manage it as effectively
as possible to speed your return to sport.

If you've prepared yourself properly in your base conditioning phase, maintained
that good work in your conversion and performance phases and balanced out your
training in your chill-out phases, ideally you shouldn't get many injuries to your body.
And by getting the basics right, good basic alignment and body position, you're not
only helping prevent injury, but also helping your actual performance: if you expend
less energy on trying to stabilise your body and hold everything in place as you move,
more energy is available to the "big" muscles that are giving you power and speed in
your athletic performance. You're more efficient, you're not wasting energy. But if you
break down and get injured, make sure you get a postural analysis done to see what's
going on - you can't always just treat the symptom.

Of course there are some chance injuries in sport that you just can't avoid, particularly
if you play a high contact sport - although the better your posture and alignment, the
better equipped your body is to withstand contact. In a rugby game, for instance, there
are times when you're going to be tackled hard and that sheer, smashing force is going
to injure you. If you're body's in good balance, it will handle a big hit better and not be
as prone to breaking down, but, to a degree, injury is a fact of life in many sports.

Also bear in mind that some sports itineraries these days aren't very realistic - which is unfortunate. Some sports administrators don't allow enough time between games for the athlete's body to fully recover, which over time can also lead to players breaking down. If this is the case, players need to speak out if they want the situation to improve.

When your body has a weakness in one area, it usually tries to compensate for it by increasing the workload of other areas. For example, there may be an increase in the stress on the back. This is one of the reasons why it's so important to be diligent in training and maintaining functional strength through the core of your body.

If you do get injured, it's important to manage it properly, to do everything in your power not only to fix the injury, but to avoid worsening the injury or areas that might be weakened or affected by the injury as you seek to rehabilitate it. This means you have to be:

- patient
- sensible
- dedicated
- mentally prepared to deal with frustration
- mentally prepared to deal with coaches or players who may push you to keep playing while you're injured (don't)
- mentally prepared to accept good medical advice.

It's easier said than done, but if you're injured, fixing that injury should be your prime concern - not the games you're missing or the player taking your place.

Of course, you should be concerned not only with the injury itself, but with the imbalances which may have caused the injury to happen in the first place. Here's a real life case in point.

There was a very good young player who burst onto the New Zealand rugby scene in 1996. He was young and talented and took the country by storm. But he had also been training in the gym without adequate supervision and had developed a postural problem. As a result, he developed chronic lower back pain. He tried to ignore it and kept on playing, but the movement patterns and the stress on his body caused by playing and training only pulled his posture further out of balance, which of course exposed him to further injury. Finally, he was in so much pain that he couldn't play. In fact, he could hardly get out of bed. The injury ended up putting him out of most rugby for the following year: he lost the chance to play for the All Blacks. Instead he had to go back and do corrective postural training to look after an injury - and as anyone who's had lower back pain will tell you, it's not an easy injury to live with. But if he'd addressed the injury when he first felt it (or better still, had his posture analysed and corrected before he started training), he might only have been out of the game for a matter of weeks.

At the beginning of 1997, Zinzan Brooke was carrying a major injury (in his groin), from the previous season, but because he handled it patiently and correctly he ended up missing very few games all year.

Margot Butcher

Zinny doesn't use a lot of machines in training, but this one was useful to isolate, work and strengthen little muscles like the gluteus medius (which stabilises the hips) when he had a groin injury.

Zinny had to go right back to basics. He didn't do any performance training (the injury limited what he could do, in any case) and in the early stages of his rehabilitation (which coincided with his base conditioning phase) he couldn't even go for a run without aggravating his body.

His emphasis was on managing the injury with targeted rehabilitation work, isolating areas around the injury to try to make it better and strengthening his posture. He also had to do a lot of lower abdominal and stabilisation work on Swiss balls that he'd never done before, exercises that made him really focus on his posture, alignment and the little muscles he used in movement.

The difficulty was that at the same time Zinny didn't want to lose too much overall fitness or strength, to become unfit while waiting for the injury to heal. Many sportspeople find themselves in this situation sooner or later and it's here that having an objective, experienced and sensible personal trainer is invaluable. He or she can help you understand the process and how the body works, minimising the frustration and helping you see the overall picture.

Most injury rehabilitation is simply about strengthening weak areas that have "gone" on you, but injury rehab is not always just for *current* injuries to your body. It can also involve past injuries. Sometimes parts you think may be "right" in fact show up in your postural analysis as potentially problem-causing. You will need to build corrective exercise into your training to address it.

Note, too, that simply going to your physio and thinking that they will fix it with a few treatments is only fooling yourself. Physiotherapists are necessary for correct diagnosis of injury and intitial treatment. You then need to work in with the physiotherapy and a good rehab trainer to fully rehabilitate your injury to the point where you have fixed the problem *functionally*, ready for sporting action again. Don't try and shorten the process - it doesn't work.

ZINZAN BROOKE:
"I have only one message as far as injury is concerned:

Fix it.

Whether they're little injuries or majors, just get them fixed. Find out what's wrong by seeking out a doctor or physiotherapist who has your physical wellbeing at heart and take their advice.

Naturally you've got to do all your warm-ups, cool-downs, stretches, posture training - all the things that prevent injury if you can. You can also prevent some stupid injuries just by being smart and wearing a mouthguard and headgear, although headgear may not prevent concussion. But I always tell people to always wear a mouthguard, even if it's uncomfortable at first. You get used to it.

The first time I injured myself it was 100 per cent stupid. I was 14 and I did a cartilage - because I'd been thoughtless and worn boots with long sprigs on a dry, rock-hard ground. When the sprigs got caught in little potholes, the little divots in this hard ground, my foot stayed in the ground as I turned around and I twisted my knee. I learned the hard way that you've got to make sure that all the gear that you're using is right for the conditions - so you've got to make sure you've got all the gear. That injury was so preventable.

I didn't completely learn my lesson though because I've done quite a few silly things over the years that I wouldn't recommend to anybody. In 1993, for instance, I had a bad sciatic nerve that I didn't look after when I should have. I'd won my test spot back the year before, under Laurie Mains, but then the sciatic nerve played up when I turned up to play against the British Lions. Because I didn't want to give up my hard-won place in the test team, I played on my sciatic nerve. Consequently my form dropped and I got axed. I cut my own throat. I was too stubborn.

But I still didn't learn from my mistake - one that very many people make. I developed a symphosis pubis (groin) injury and actually played through most of 1996 with it, even though I couldn't really stride out. Thankfully it came right in the end, but that was only because I was bloody lucky. I didn't do the right thing by playing on it. I should have stopped instead, worked on rehab and got it fixed. Imagine not being part of the All Blacks in 1996! It was a very special year and I was foolish risking that. I should have respected my body and thought about what was really right for me in the long run, if I really wanted to be sure of being there for the special games.

The thing was, when I first noticed discomfort during the 1996 Super 12, I thought it was "just a little groin injury". I thought it would go away. But I didn't have the expertise to diagnose it myself and it turned out to be an injury that affected my whole groin area. In the end it hurt so much that I couldn't even get out of bed properly - I had to train myself to roll off the bed onto my knees and then stand up. I couldn't do anything, really. I even found it hard to push weights, so I had to train myself to keep doing the weights, but not tighten up my stomach as I did them, because it used to hurt so much.

The other major injury that affected me was the Achilles tendon I partially tore before the 1995 World Cup. Once again, same old story of a player being too stubborn for his own good. I'd had a really sore Achilles when I was playing for the Harlequins before that, a game we won by 80 points. I pretended that that meant it was OK to keep playing. I didn't treat it right, and it also wasn't diagnosed right and consequently I ruptured it.

After carrying that injury through the 1995 World Cup, I was going to retire. I felt terrible - mentally shattered from the strain of it. I sat down when we came back and thought, 'Geez, I don't play rugby to feel like this!'. I wasn't enjoying my rugby at all. But I'd stupidly put myself in that situation. I needed someone bigger than me to say, 'Zinny, get yourself right, forget the World Cup, you're not in the right condition to play.' Instead I made that same old classic, pig-headed mistake of telling myself I was right when I really wasn't, giving myself that chance to come right again and again.

Of course it's hard. If you're competitive, and sportspeople are competitive people, you want to think that you can beat the injury. Then you play the big games and the adrenalin takes hold, you want to be part of it. It's very hard to stand yourself back and say, 'Just be patient, sit it out". You don't want to miss out on that moment and you may not want to give someone else a chance to take your place. When you're in sport, and you're suddenly on the outside looking in, instead of taking the field or being in the dressing room warming up, it's never the same. The team's doing something you're not: you're excluded from the experiences they're sharing.

But that's when you have to be tough, if you really shouldn't be playing because you're body's out of balance. You might think that it's being "tough" to be able to play on an injury, but I say that it's actually mentally tougher to sit it out and deal with injuries when you need to, not when you have no choice. Players have to be a bit hard on themselves. You really need to be a little bit selfish instead of thinking, 'Argh, I know I'm injured, but I really want to play this game', or, 'But I really want to be there for the team....'

As a professional rugby player, every time I take the field it's a business decision. If I go and play on an injury and stuff it up, it could be the end of my career, the end of my earning capacity - but I should have been jolted into thinking more about managing my body properly long before professionalism came along in rugby. You'll last longer in the long run if you just fix your injuries straight away instead of leaving them.

Not everyone understands, of course, and what's especially disappointing is there are still a lot of coaches and sports doctors around who don't get it. I've seen with my own eyes too many players who have been pressured into playing on an injury, by the coach, for example, in situations where they shouldn't have been playing at all. It happens a lot at all levels and I've seen it wreck guys' careers. They end up exiting through the back door with their body in a mess and their reputation as a player compromised by the poor form they showed when they weren't right.

Sure, some guys are wrapped in cotton wool and need to be pushed through that comfort zone to perform (we call them suction-gutses - they need physio and massages all day), but there's a difference between pushing yourself and risking yourself. You can push yourself through that pain barrier, but if you do that on an injury, you're just stupid. It's shortsighted. You'll pay for it. Instead you've got to stand up for yourself, be a little selfish and strong if your body's not ready to play.

When you've got an injury, you've got to talk to people who care about you - which may not always be your coach or rugby people who want to see you on the park. Talk to doctors, people who are objective and who are definitely going to point you in the right direction.

Some players find it difficult to talk about their injuries. They feel they have to push themselves through that barrier of pain that the injury throws up in their face. But that's just being in denial. It's not that hard to say to someone, 'Hey Doc, I'm a bit worried about this pain in my shoulder when I hit the scrum, or, 'This tightness in my leg, what is it?'. That's how you start finding out what's happening so you can work on it. Too many players actually have to get injured further to realise they have to stop. You can be so much smarter.

I know I haven't always set the best example, but because I've been through it and know how much it stuffs you up, I hope that other players will listen to me and not have to make the mistake for themselves to understand.

When I had my groin injury, I definitely didn't treat it right in the beginning and took the attitude that it was just a little injury and would come right with a bit of massage and physiotherapy. I was looking after it between Super 12 games, but because I was training and playing on it, it got a little bit worse. Then I started training for and playing the Western Samoan test match, then the Scotland tests in 1996. After that game I had an injection in my groin, either a cortisone or a local anaesthetic, just to settle it down. We had a couple of weeks' break. Then we played Australia down in Wellington and South Africa in Christchurch and so on and it never came right all season. The desire to play against South Africa became greater than the injury. I ignored how my body was feeling and kept getting cortisone or local anaesthetic injections in my groin, before each of the last five tests that year.

But my body was out of balance, and an injection can't fix that. I couldn't do half of what I wanted to. I couldn't accelerate off the mark, I was slow and sluggish. When I had my last injection after that final game in Johannesburg, I said, "I'm never having an injection to play again". It was the wrong thing to do, for me in that situation.

Then I took a couple of weeks off and then came back for the NPC. I was still sort of battling through it, but I wasn't happy at all. I'd tried to let time heal it, but it never did. That was because what I actually needed to do was take steps to correct the injury, not just leave it alone. So at the end of the year I got back into the gym to start some strengthening exercises.

I did some tests and found out I was really weak through my front area (I failed all my abdominal tests) and that my posture was wrong - my hips were starting to roll forward. I was walking around as if I had a pot gut and my stomach muscles were so weak that I was walking with a duck bum, everything at the wrong angle. All that was the result of not managing my groin injury well in the first place. I hadn't been able to train that whole area, so I had lost balance. My body was compensating for the injury in other areas - everything was getting screwed up. My step shortened up: I was hopping along instead of striding.

So if you've got an injury, get it sorted. I've learned to look at it bluntly. I'm in the game *because I enjoy it, but it's also my job and my income. These days, if I manage my body well, I can earn a lot of money playing rugby and everyone knows that. But if you're reckless, you're going to be history before your time. You'll exit through the back door. I've seen it happen to players already. So my philosophy is just be sensible about it, be professional about it, be patient and deal with injuries when they happen. It will cost you money to get it right, to see the physios and so on as often as you need, but it's an investment in your future in the game.*

Jonah Lomu's a good example of the approach you should take if something's not right with your body. The greatest thing that's ever happened to Jonah is that everyone knows what's been wrong with him now. People used to say, 'What the hell's wrong with Jonah?' before they found out he had a serious kidney condition. There was pressure on him from outside to play. Obviously he had to take himself out of that situation and for eight months he had to be selfish, make himself unavailable to play. Jonah's a dramatic example, but that's exactly what you must do, essentially, if you develop an injury that affects your balance, strength and form.

If you still need convincing, let me warn you that rehab work can be the hardest work you'll ever do.

When I had my Achilles tendon, I had to do a lot of water running. I'd do it for 40 minutes and I had to train hard, getting my heart rate up to 160 or 170, because I needed to get my aerobic fitness up as well as fix the injury. It was so hard that I was actually sweating in the pool. I had to do that every morning for five weeks. It was monotonous and hard work and I would find myself getting wound up very easily. If someone played the wrong chord around me, I snapped. I don't recommend that situation to anyone. If you can avoid that stress and strain by managing your injury sensibly in the first place, do it.

Having an injury doesn't usually mean a complete lay-off. If you talk with your trainer, there's always something you can do in training, alternatives you can try while you're tending an injury. When I had my groin injury, I was still able to do my legs and my water-running and my upper body strength. I could still do all my shoulder exercises that were able to provide strength for tackling and taking the ball up. I couldn't get on a rowing machine and really pull up, because I'd have to tense my abdominal muscles, so it was a question of finding something to do instead.

Finally, "no pain, no gain" is just an old cliché, a load of rubbish. It's appropriate sometimes, when you're strong and fit, but it doesn't refer to when you have an injury. Go to the edge of safety, sure, but then back off a bit. That's the key. Listen to your body, don't be stupid. I've learned that from experience."

chapter (7)

Avoiding Burnout and Overtraining

*I*n chapter two we learned that improved sports performance is a result of the work you do in training and the rest that you allow between the work. Therefore, the benefits of training are maximised by getting the right type and amount of rest. But one of the commonest mistakes people - particularly young, keen and eager sportspeople - make in training is to work themselves too hard, without taking time to allow their bodies to regenerate between sessions. This is what we call overtraining.

Many people don't realise when they're overtraining. It doesn't stop you training - in fact, you may be able to continue training harder. But your body won't actually be getting the results it should. Walk into any gym in the country and you'll probably see a young man who can't understand why he's not getting much bigger or stronger from weight-training his legs or his chest heavily two or three times a week. It's because he simply isn't allowing enough time for those muscle groups to recover and repair themselves at a cellular level. Instead he's training himself in an overtrained state.

TRAINING SMARTER, NOT HARDER

There's just no point training a body that hasn't fully recovered from the work it did a day, two days or a week ago. It's therefore important to ensure that you don't overtrain, that you have periods in which your body can fully recover from its effort. These may be days off (i.e. days with no exercise) or light days (days with easy or light exercise, with your usual intensity and/or the volume of exercise reduced), or days doing a different type of activity (easy, refreshing laps of a pool, for example, or an enjoyable run).

It actually takes the nervous system, which includes your mind, longer to recover than muscles. So, from day to day or week to week, your muscles might recover quite

NZ Herald/Brett Phibbs

Variety in your training is an important ingredient in avoiding burnout. Here the All Blacks swap a lineout and scrum session for an aerobics workout - note Zinny's great flexibility and technique!

quickly. You'll replace glycogen - your muscles' fuel - through the food that you eat and you'll drink lots of water which will help clean them out. But the nervous system operates completely differently. That's why we don't hammer ourselves in training week after week, training like a madman.

We need hard days and easy days, hard weeks and easier weeks - even if it's two hard weeks followed by an easy week. It's actually on the *easy* days that we get fitter and stronger, because that's when the body recovers enough to reap the benefits from the training it's been doing. This strategy (which is loading and unloading) needs to be put in place from the beginning of your training to ensure that you don't overtrain.

No matter how strong or athletic you believe yourself to be, overtraining is not only a waste of effort and time, but it will be just a matter of time before you're mentally or emotionally fatigued and physically injured. An overtrained athlete is no good to anyone, least of all to themselves.

So how do you tell if you're getting into an overtrained state? Every athlete is different, but these are some of the general indicators you can watch out for:

- Not enough sleep, or broken sleep
- A loss of appetite
- An increased morning heart rate (pulse)
- How sore the body feels (aches, tiredness, constantly heavy legs)
- How you feel emotionally and mentally
- Poor concentration
- Struggling willpower
- What your ability to relax and laugh is like (loss of humour)
- How you react to other people - are you tetchy or irritable?
- Loss of sex drive.

Keep these points in mind (note them in your training diary) from the beginning of your training. It will help you build up a picture of what you are like as an athlete mentally, physically and emotionally, making it easier to identify when you're out of sorts. Remember that your training programme is a *guideline*, that it's flexible and that you've got to be prepared to step back and listen to what your body's telling you, how it's handling training, competition and stress.

If you *are* feeling overtrained, it's time to have a break, back off, and then start training a little smarter. Here are some options and remedies to help you get back on track:

- Stop training for a while (e.g. one week)
- Relax - chill out
- Train easier for a while
- Do a different type of training activity
- Put the fun back into your training and life
- Make time for massage / spas (hot tubs) / stretching
- Take time out from the general training environment
- Plan your time better.

TRAINING AND YOUR LIFESTYLE

For most people training is only a part of their daily life, so stress and pressures from outside the training environment can also affect the quality of your training, making you feel overtrained at times.

If things aren't going well at school, tech, university or work or you have too many assignments or deadlines, if you're smoking or drinking or staying up late or watching too much TV, if you're having relationship difficulties, if you're not eating well, if you have a health problem, a cold, a sore throat - any of these stress factors can compromise your ability to recover effectively from your training.

Therefore you're not only training yourself to listen to your body, to recognise how much energy, zest and spark it has on a particular day, but to understand the effects of your lifestyle on your body and mind.

HOW YOUR RECOVERY STRATEGIES WORK

Massage and stretching are two recovery strategies that are so simple that they're often underestimated.

Massage is one of best recovery (and preventative) measures an athlete can take. With exercise, your muscles often become naturally tight or "knotty".

Massage frees the muscle up. It gets the circulation moving through it. It also helps unblock all the little knots of scar tissue (scar tissue doesn't function as well as normal muscle tissue, so this is clearly important to the athlete) and helps speed the repair of the little tears it might have suffered. With massage you're stretching and restoring your muscle fibres to their normal length, structure and consistency so that they're at their optimum elasticity and they aren't full of these little blockages that inhibit their ability to work properly.

Without regular massage, over time your muscles tend not to work as well. They become a little stiffer, they don't contract as well and the blood supply through them is more inhibited than in a normal, resilient muscle.

As a bonus, massage also has a great effect on your nervous system. Everyone knows how good it feels when somebody even just rubs your shoulders. It takes away some stress and tension, relaxes you. Your body is all connected as one, so treating your nervous system to a massage is genuinely therapeutic to an athlete.

While massage will assist your nervous system and muscles, regular stretching will take good care of most of your connective tissue (like your tendons), keeping it nice and supple. Some athletes use yoga for this purpose.

Try incorporating a weekly massage and daily stretching into your programme. If you're not sure where to go for a sports massage (or 'therapeutic massage'), try the noticeboard at your local gym or health food shop. Many gyms have a professional massage service on the same premises.

Of course, getting good sleep, nutrition (food) and hydration (fluids) are also important factors in effective recovery and these should become basic to your daily life.

THE FUN FACTOR

When did you first start to train? Many of you may answer that it was a week ago, a month ago or a year ago, but you're all wrong. In fact you started training when you were a baby.

We *all* begin training when we're babies. We pick ourselves up and begin to crawl, begin to walk, begin to run and fall over, practising, trying things out and resting in between. And as the smile on any baby's face will tell you, it's fun!

But as we get older, we lose the fun of it. We adults tend to be serious about our pursuits and ambitions and can too easily become intense and single-minded. However, because the process of training for sports performance is hard work, it helps to maintain an element of fun in training: it helps keep you going, taking your mind off the pain, and biochemically stimulates the body. Somewhere in your training process, if you bring in laughter, fun and games, suddenly it doesn't seem so stressful. Laughter releases natural biochemicals that relax your system and make you feel good.

As a trainer, telling a joke, making people laugh in a training session is one way I can get a better performance out of them. You just can't have training sessions that are so focused that all the sportsperson is ever thinking about is their training and performance. There has to be balance there. It's very important. You recover better when you're relaxed and you recover better from stress when you laugh, so training must be part of your optimum lifestyle rather than simply a means to an end.

The more games and the more fun you can put into training, the better. One of the ways to do this is to make creative use of that quality that almost all sportspeople possess: their natural competitiveness.

Zinzan Brooke is one of the most competitive people I've ever met in my life. *Everything* with him is a competition - and he's competitive in everything. But he doesn't take it to the the point where, if he doesn't win, he gets angry or bitter or resentful. He also has a huge ability to laugh, even at himself.

All Blacks often use little games in their training. Here's an example. Sean Fitzpatrick and Zinzan Brooke use a particular acceleration drill that help them develop quickness off the mark - the first few metres are all important in their sport.

One person stands behind another at a set distance apart: the goal then is for the person behind to try and tag the person in front of them before the latter crosses a line. We set that game up as a contest - the best of 10, with a rest period between each attempt - and it quickly becomes very competitive. Each tries to win. They try to put each other off, to outsmart each other, to be tougher and faster - and they also share laughter in between attempts.

When Zinzan was chasing Sean on one particular occasion, you could see that Sean had really got off the mark quite well, while Zinny had conversely been a little slow to react. So Zinny yelled out, "Ha, ha, gotcha!". He actually wasn't near Sean at all, but by doing this he got inside Sean's head. Sean responded by moving into a more defensive posture (trying to make it difficult for Zinny to touch him from behind) and sure enough Zinny tagged him before he got to the mark!

You can imagine that an All Black has a lot of stress placed on them to perform well, not only from the public, but from the players looking to take their place and from the very high standards they set for themselves and that the coach sets for them: if they can have fun in training, that reduces the stress in their lives. It helps their emotional response to training and their physical reactions as well.

This is what Zinzan Brooke has to say about the importance of having a sense of fun and balance in his daily life:

ZINZAN BROOKE:
"As an athlete, you probably know that you want to be flexible physically, but you have to learn to be flexible mentally as well. One of the most important mental skills is to be able to just switch off. It's actually really hard to train your brain to get away from the training mindset when training's over for the day, but that's certainly what I had to learn to do.

Lee's right when he says I'm naturally very competitive. I've been making a contest, a game of things for as long as I can remember. Like, before one of the All Black tests in 1997 I challenged Justin Marshall to see if he could drink more water than me before the match (because it's good to be really well hydrated when you play). Neither of us would give in and it was a way of making an important little preparation thing fun. It's the same in the gym. In between exercises I might challenge "Junior" Tonu'u to see how many times he can kick a Swiss ball around a pillar, putting spin on it with his foot. That's training a skill, being competitive and having fun all at the same time.

But with that there, that diehard competitive nature, you really do have to know how to switch off from the training and from the game, as well.

I didn't know how to do that when I was younger. For a long time, even when I first got in the All Blacks, I used to think about the game constantly from Saturday night right through to the next game next week. Then I'd arrive at the ground Saturday afternoon and I'd be yawning my head off in the changing room, really tired. I'd think, 'Geez, I've done all this bloody mental preparation and I feel shot! What's my problem?' But I'd actually zapped my brain so much, concentrated so hard on rugby without any breaks that after the game I'd just crash because my brain was mush. I also didn't eat properly back then and that definitely had a bad effect on me as well. The combination of burning myself out mentally and not fuelling my body was a recipe for trouble.

So you've got to learn to be able to switch off when you're not training. You've got to learn to have your breaks during the week and during the days leading up to the game. It's like, don't take your work home. It's a hard thing to train yourself to do. Like for me, in my position, I've always tried to get the edge, tried to think about beating someone, tried to think, 'OK, I'm playing this team this week, how am I going to beat this team? What can I take to training on a Tuesday, what can I take to training on a Thursday that's going to make us a better team? What can I discuss with the coach, what can I say to the players?'

But when I do that mental preparation, I've learned now to actually get my ideas out in training, and then when training's over, I stop thinking about them for a while. You've got to shut it down and go about doing your normal things, otherwise it burns you down. Get away from it. Train on a Tuesday at 4 o'clock till 6 o'clock, have a think about what you've done and then let it go.

I do firmly believe that leading up to a game, your mental preparation has to still be done during the week. There are very few players around who don't need to mentally prepare, who get to a game and just switch on. But like everything in training, you have to manage that preparation correctly, manage your time and make it fit in with the overall picture. So if you're thinking about practice or the game coming up, that's fine, but draw a line and conciously turn your attention to something else after a while.

Every player's different, so you've got to figure out and learn what works best for you. Switching off works for me. I'm not going to get a better performance from thinking about my game non-stop all week - I'm going to get a worse performance.

I'm quite relaxed before games. This is another aspect of finding the right balance. Once upon a time, before test matches I used to think that you had to sit in your room getting yourself all worked up and tense about it, that you had to sit on the bus with a frown on your face and not look at the public out the window. It was an old image that you thought you had to adhere to. But then I thought, what is this actually doing for me? It wasn't doing me any good at all. I feel I'm ready to play better if I'm relaxed, not tense, beforehand - and it's out there on the dancefloor that you have to dance, after all, not on the bus or wherever beforehand.

I think that the ability to relax and keep your balance mentally could be the x-factor that lets you perform better than your opposition. I've been on New Zealand Maori tours where we've been playing the guitar on the bus, going to the game, telling jokes an hour before kick-off, having a laugh - and we've played out of our skins.

I think the same applies to practice, not just games. Like, why do you do trainings on Tuesdays and Thursdays? You train to perfect the things you do on Saturday. So why is it on Tuesday and Thursday you can be nice and relaxed in training, but you can't be relaxed on a Saturday? You've still got to focus and concentrate, but having a laugh with someone in between doesn't mean you're not taking it seriously. Laughing can be an expression that actually you've done all your mental preparation and that you're relaxed and in a good state of mind.

I believe there's got to be room in a team for individuals to express themselves, too. If you're the sort of person who likes to whistle or put on your headphones and listen to music in the changing room, you shouldn't be pressured by other people to "act more focused".

Margot Butcher

Zinny's not a great fan of running, but enjoys it more if he runs through a pleasant park like the Auckland Domain with a training partner for motivation (here it's Auckland rep Dylan Mika).

Take Counties' Jimmy Coe. I played with Jimmy Coe in the New Zealand Colts, and in the 1997 Auckland Blues. When we warmed up before games, Jimmy Coe never warmed up with the team. He just sat there in a corner. Sometimes before games he'd just sit and polish guys' shoes while we were doing all these grids, working up a sweat, passing the ball, yelling to each other. He just waits. But then he runs on and plays a blinder! It cracks me up, but it works for him. It might not work for me, but it works for him, so I respect that. Players have to try new methods and use what works for them - and it doesn't necessarily have to be what everyone else is doing. There's all sorts of different recipes for the same cake: you've just got to find the right mixture for yourself.

I'm also a big believer in being willing to enjoy variety in your training. Training does have to be hard sometimes, but you can tailor it to make it as stimulating and enjoyable to you as possible. I don't like running much for example, but I enjoy it more if I run with a mate, I run through a nice track with lots of trees and birds around early in the morning and if I jump into a hot tub afterwards. You have to use your imagination.

Sometimes when I go to the gym, I just don't feel like doing the exercises that are in front of me, so I ask Lee if I can train other parts of my body, or do something I haven't done before, or do a bench press instead of jump on the rowing machine. I like that sense of variety not just in the gym, but in my training week. With the All Blacks and the Blues, for instance, I used to sometimes try to think of training exercises we could do other than just practising scrummaging and lineouts. One day we didn't tell anyone in the team what we would be doing, we just told them all to meet for training down at Mission Bay instead of Eden Park. When they arrived we put them into teams, got into double kayaks and paddled over to North Head, jumped out, ran around North Head, paddled back over to Kohimarama, ran around a rugby ground there, went for another paddle and went back to the drop-off point. Some of the guys found that really interesting. It broke up the routine of training in a long season.

Margot Butcher

Always make time to stretch before and after any training session.

You can do this within training as well - we might play 'softball rugby', or Aussie Rules, or Gaelic or touch to make training interesting, so guys don't lose enthusiasm. Those kinds of games are still using skills that you need in rugby. You're not doing something else for the sake of doing something completely different: what you're trying to do is combine the skill of your sport with a new idea. It stimulates you emotionally, stimulates your brain. After all, there's nothing worse than going to training week after week for 10 months knowing you're going to do exactly the same stuff time after time.

I always ask the guys, "What would you like to do for training, would you like to do something different? Would you like to go for a row?' Then I go to the management and see what they think. Like the All Blacks did aerobics before one of our tests in 1997 and it was bloody good! Guys got away from that boredom of hitting rucks and scrums for a little while.

The reality is that training is a job at any level, but it can be made a chore. That's the thing you've got to get away from. Coaches and trainers can help you do that. They have to "feel" the athlete, understand what they're going through emotionally and physically so they understand when it's the right time to say, 'OK, don't come to training on Tuesday, have a day off and see you Thursday'. If a coach said that to me in the middle of a heavy season, say after the All Black season when I still had the NPC to go, I'd immediately think 'Great, he's thinking about my wellbeing' and feel very positive and enthusiastic when I came back. As long as it's at the right time, of course.

On this note I feel that when a player is respected and there's no hidden agendas, the player will do the job and they'll honour the team and the coach, put their body on the line for something they believe in. But I think some coaches don't "feel" the players. I've seen really good examples where players have been pushed through situations they shouldn't have to have been put in. The coaches obviously are thinking about their own neck, the results they need to seek week by week, match by match. I think it's wrong. You have to have good managerial skills and not just think about yourself as a coach using players to notch up a win. We all want to win, but you've got to do it with a certain passion and decorum, enjoyment. Sometimes, if you feel bored, flat or perhaps overtrained, you just have to take time out to get back that spark.

Finally, if you're feeling a bit under the weather with a cold or the flu, I think it's a fallacy that you should 'sweat it out'. You're better to have time off and get yourself right than push yourself through it in training. You've got to tell your coach or doctor that you're not feeling well and get in bed and look after your body. If I've got the flu, I listen to my body, sleep as much as the body wants.

Go to the old mechanic shop and fix it. That's the message.'

chapter (8)

Sports Nutrition, Hydration and Supplementation

*T*here's no doubt that to achieve optimal sports performance, your body must be functioning at its best. We've already looked at ways of managing your body effectively in training to help the brain, bones, muscles, joints and energy systems function at their best, but the way you fuel your body with food and water also has a great effect on the way it will perform for you.

> *BETTER NUTRITION = BETTER BODY = BETTER PERFORMANCE*

Your body is constantly repairing and rebuilding itself. As we've mentioned, over the span of one year approximately 98 per cent of all the molecules in your body are completely replaced. The body you have today has been built almost entirely from what you have eaten over the last six months. It follows, then, that the quality of food you eat over a long period of time is very important to the quality of your body and its performance in sport.

Nutrition is quite an individual thing. We're all different. We all like and dislike different foods, and not only that, but our "food upbringing" and even ethnicity can have an affect on our ability to digest some foods better than others. Most people have an inherent tendency to handle some foods better than other people, and tendencies to want particular foods that may not work for the person next to them. Some are also vegetarian - if that's you, you must make sure you consult a qualified sports nutritionist before you embark on training because you will need to pay special attention to the way you fuel your body.

So we don't believe in setting hard and fast rules about nutrition in the sense of writing down a diet that you should adhere to as an athlete. It simply doesn't work. Give 15 rugby players an identical, strict sports food plan and you'll probably find that the benefits they gain from it vary widely (and they'll get bored, because they won't need to use their imagination to put good food together for themselves). There are certain scientifically-proven guidelines that work for all people, sure, but don't discount the individual factor.

So what are these guidelines?

WHAT TO EAT

Poor quality food builds a poor quality structure in your body, so your overall aim is to constantly eat mostly high nutrient food.

Much of the food we eat today is not what it should be. Many foods have become "degraded" in nutrients, which means that your body must work harder to get nutrients from food, or may not get the nutrients that it needs from it at all.

Food becomes degraded by:

- A loss of nutrients in the soil in which food is grown
- A loss of nutrients during food processing
- Contamination (by bacteria, for example)
- Too much fat in food
- Too much salt or sugar in food (especially processed food).

It follows that processed food is generally less useful to you as an athlete than freshly prepared or "whole" food.

Your first step in organising optimal nutrition should be to digest and use this food pyramid:

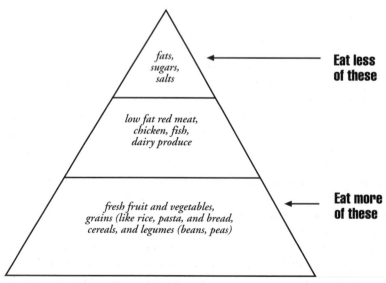

You'll see that good quality grains, fruit and vegetables are the foundation of good health and performance, along with moderate servings of low-fat, high-quality proteins. As we'll see later, you can also exercise a choice between "good fat" and "bad fat" in your diet, and this is important.

CARBOHYDRATES

Athletes need to have a good understanding of the carbohydrate, protein and fat content of their food choices.

Carbohydrates are a class of food which the body breaks down into glucose (a simple sugar). It sends the glucose into the bloodstream to act as fuel for your muscles. Glucose is stored in muscles or in the liver (as glycogen - groups of glucose molecules joined together), while excess glucose is stored as fat.

An adequate supply of carbohydrates (fuel) is essential for optimal performance and recovery. It's like putting the best fuel into your car for optimal performance.

Often you'll hear carbohydrates described as either "simple carbohydrates" or "complex carbohydrates", which describes the molecular structure that the body must digest, break down. But that's really an old, out-of-date way of analysing your fuel. For the purpose of optimal sports performance, it's more useful to look at what we call the "glycemic index" of carbohydrates.

The glycemic index is simply the rate at which sugars from food are released into the bloodstream: or how quickly your muscles can get energy from food.

Foods with a low glycemic index provide a steady, slow release of sugars to the body, ensuring a constant supply and even energy levels. They load our muscles ready for exercise. Foods with a high glycemic index provide a much quicker supply of sugars to the body, raising our blood sugar levels rapidly. They are ideal for replacing muscle glycogen (sugars) after exercise.

An experienced trainer or nutritionist can help you understand the glycemic index of your food, but here's a few examples to help you choose what to eat when.

FOOD WITH A HIGH GLYCEMIC INDEX	FOOD WITH A LOW GLYCEMIC INDEX
White bread, wholemeal bread	Mixed grain bread
Cornflakes, Nutrigrain, Sustain	All Bran, Special K, Porridge
Calrose rice	White rice
Weetbix, ricebubbles, cornflakes	Pasta / noodles
Bananas, watermelon, raisins	Oranges, pears, apricots, grapes
Parsnips, swedes	Carrots, kumara, yams, apples
Baked potato, French fries	Baked beans
Hydrafuel	Whole milk
Lucozade, Coca-Cola, Powerade	Apple juice, grapefruit juice
Muesli bar	
Honey, sugar, jellybeans	

A high-carbohydrate diet is essential in sport as it ensures the athlete has large stores of muscle glycogen and energy. Therefore an athlete's basic training diet should be based around carbohydrate foods with a *low* glycemic index to ensure good stores of glycogen and constant blood sugar levels. But after training or playing, an athlete will need high glycemic index foods to give a faster rate of recovery and replenishment.

Here's an example of how you might manage your carbohydrate intake on a training or playing day:

1. **Before Exercise**
   - Eat a supply of low glycemic index carbs three to four hours before training or playing.
   - Avoid eating sugar.
   - Remember you are loading your muscle glycogen stores for exercise - your body prefers to use muscle glycogen stores from food consumed three or four hours ago than to use sugar that you have only recently eaten.

2. **During Exercise**
   - Sip water or a five to 10 per cent carbohydrate rehydration drink to avoid dehydration and a drop in blood glucose levels.

3. **After Exercise**
   - First, drink plain water to rehydrate (water also helps alkalise the body after exercise, which creates an acidic state in the body).
   - Have a carbohydrate drink that contains a little sugar (glucose, fructose) to rapidly aid muscle glycogen replacement. Avoid so-called sports drinks that exceed 12% in sugars. These don't allow an adequate absorption of water and carbohydrate and therefore have an opposite and detrimental effect to their claims.
   - Or, eat high glycemic index carbohydrates.
   - Later, after one or two hours, eat low glycemic index carbs to continue loading your muscles with fuel (readying them for your next training session).

FATS

Fat is important for performance and health, but you need to manage your fat intake wisely, which includes monitoring the amount of fat you eat. There are good fats and bad fats, and those people who want the best performing bodies need to understand the difference between the two.

Modern food processing (creating 'concocted' foods such as chocolate bars, margarine and pre-made salad dressing) often changes good, healthy, usable fats into harmful fats that are not only damaging to the body's structure, but are unsuitable for providing optimal performance. The altered chemical structure of these "bad fats" means they are too difficult for the body to easily digest and use.

Bad fats are created when foods are heated, hydrogenised, bleached or deodorised, for example, in processing, so you need to think carefully about how foods have been prepared before you buy them off the supermarket shelves.

Here's a guideline that should get you thinking about the way you eat fat:

FATS TO EAT	FATS TO REDUCE
Organic flax seed oil	Most processed cooking oil
Olive oil	Margarine
Those in sardines, salmon, fish in general	Butter
Borage Oil	High fat dairy products
Canola Oil	Fatty red meats
Evening Primrose Oil	Sausages
Those in scallops, mussels	Bacon
Those in turkey, skinless chicken	Commercial burgers, meat pies
Those in whole grain bread	Fish'n'chips
Those in low-fat dressings	Potato chips (i.e. crisps and fried)
Those in cottage cheese	High-fat dressings
	Muffins (if made with butter not olive oil)
	High fat desserts, chocolate, biscuits

The message about fat is just be sensible. Most of us know what is fattening and what is not, after all. The above is simply a guideline, so use it as one. If performance is important to you, then eat with moderation in mind. Splurge out now and again, but don't make it a habit. It *is* important to relax now and again, to chill out and enjoy. But remember, good fuel and staying at the right bodyweight are essential to optimal performance at any level.

PROTEIN

After water, protein is more plentiful than any other substance in the body. Protein is of primary important to the growth and development of your body (as well as being important in maintaining a healthy immune system). All the tissues, the muscles, bones, teeth, hair, skin and everything else is made mostly out of protein.

If you eat foods containing poor quality protein, then it follows that the structures of your body will also be poor in quality. Athletes need the soundest body they can get, so they need to aim at getting adequate, good quality protein on a daily basis. Ideally these proteins should be low in fat.

Sources of good quality protein include:

- Fish, lean meats, seafood, skinless chicken, egg whites, turkey.
- Beans (vegetable protein is generally of lower quality than non-vegetable sources).
- Whey protein concentrate powders (these are by far the most superior supplement form of protein as far as commercial sports supplements go).

HOW TO EAT

Your body requires a constant supply of good nutrition to replace your fuel, rebuild tissue and perform its many vital functions. Eating small amounts often will provide a more constant flow of these nutrients than eating, say, three large meals a day. You may therefore choose to eat a medium-sized breakfast, lunch and dinner, with smaller "snack meals" in between, or four to six small meals a day. Eating small and often helps:

- Maintain consistent energy levels, necessary for training and competition
- Increase the ability of the body to burn excess fat stores (calories) by increasing metabolism
- Supply adequate protein to maintain lean muscle tissue
- Ensure adequate recovery from training and competition
- Prevent an excess intake of calories (which accumulate as body fat).

SUPPLEMENTATION

The modern world of nutritional and vitamin supplements is so complex (and so aggressively marketed) that it's easy to feel unsure about what to take and what to avoid when you first develop an interest in sports nutrition. How do you know what works and what doesn't?

Supplements should be incorporated into your nutritional plan to "fill the gaps" - that is, to address possible deficiencies in your food intake. Remember that supplements mean "as well as", not "instead of": good food is your prime source of fuel and building blocks for your body. Supplements should be added strategically, with thought given to the time at which you might need them.

Stick with reputable brand names - companies which are renowned for their research in the field. Generally you get what you pay for - a slightly higher price usually means higher quality, potency and better results.

Taking the right supplements for the right reasons can certainly be of immense benefit to your athletic performance, but before you consider taking anything, get the advice of an independent, qualified dietitian or doctor. Discuss products with them. This is especially important because any young athlete using supplements needs to make sure that they understand not only why they are taking them, but that there are no illegal contents in them, in terms of sport.

Generally speaking, the following types of supplements may be of assistance in your training and performance week:

- **Multi-Vitamin-Mineral**
  Provides essential nutrients that may be deficient in your diet. Provides extra essential nutrients that may assist in your performance and recovery.

- **Creatine Phosphate**
  Regenerates your anaerobic energy system to allow near maximal muscle contraction. An immediate increase in strength is evident. Increases your ability to work out (perform) harder. Valuable to sports where power, speed and strength are required. You must consult a qualified dietitian for the correct use of Creatine.

- **Organic Flax Seed Oil**
  Provides an ample supply of good fats (essential fatty acids).

- **Protein Powders**
  Provide high quality protein. Whey protein concentrate as the base protein source is by far the best type to go for. Avoid cheaper sources that claim to contain high amounts, but are often of lesser quality.

HYDRATION

Finally, always ensure your body has plenty of water. The quality of the tissues that make up your body is absolutely dependent on both the quality and quantity of water you drink. Make sure you drink in the time before, during and after training or playing. You may want to make a habit of carrying a "sipper bottle" of water around with you.

A good intake of water will:
- Keep your body temperature down (prevent overheating).
- Eliminate the muscles' waste products (toxins) from the body.
- Prevent dehydration.
- Prevent disruption caused by chemical imbalances.
- Keep you alert.

It's worth remembering that if a muscle dehydrates by only three per cent, it actually loses about ten per cent of its contractile strength and eight per cent of its ability to give you speed. In other words, your performance literally dries up!

Exercise increases your body temperature in direct proportion to the exercise load. Your body tries to maintain its resting temperature by moving the extra heat to the surface of your skin (via the blood). There heat dissipates into the air, mainly by the evaporation of sweat.

The higher your core body temperature rises during exercise, the more blood is used for cooling - which means less blood is available to your muscles. That's essentially why it is so important for you to drink cool water and avoid overheating and dehydration.

Margot Butcher

Always ensure your body has plenty of water.

Water Tips:

- Drink water that is as cool as possible.
- Drink often to avoid dehydration.
- Pre-hydrate: - drink extra water two days before your event
  - drink every 15-20 minutes, two to three hours before your event
  - keep drinking up to 20 minutes before your event.
- Hydrate by eating carbohydrates - they have a high water content.
- When you drink water during exercise, sip rather than gulp for maximum absorption.
- Rehydrate after exercise with plain water first.
- Drink tea, coffee and alcohol in moderation, if at all - these drinks actually dehydrate you.

PLAY IT SMART - DRINK SMART!

Nutrition is a key area in which Zinzan Brooke made changes that markedly enhanced his ability and performance as an All Black. Here's his story:

ZINZAN BROOKE

"Learning about good sports nutrition and putting it into practice allowed me to better my potential by looking after my body. But the mindset of some players (including myself) in the past was often a world away from how we think now with the benefit of modern knowledge.

This is what I used to do. I used to eat nothing but tea and a piece of toast before games because I thought that if I ate something, I'd be slow around the field. I was the person who would have a big meal the night before the game - that would be my last meal before playing, so the day of the game I'd feel really "light" and ready to go. I'd get up in the morning, have this tiny amount of breakfast and that would be it. I thought if I ate any more than that, I'd be heavy and carting it round the ground.

When you think that most games didn't kick off until 2.30pm, it was a long time for my body to go without fuel. Adrenalin seemed to take over, but adrenalin's no substitute for carbohydrates. I used to wonder sometimes why I felt stuffed when there were still 25 minutes left to go in the game and I thought I was fit. I just couldn't get round the track sometimes, even though I'd been in the All Blacks five or six years! I look back and realise that the reason I probably felt fatigued during a lot of matches wasn't because of the game, but because I hadn't put enough fuel in the tank.

We were so naive. I remember Steve McDowell used to have a big meal on the day of the game, before running out - he used to eat a big steak with eggs and all the rest of it. I used to think, 'How are you going to run around the track?' He was actually eating the wrong type of food for the day, but I didn't know any better myself. I didn't know what to eat or when to eat.

It was crazy. I wasn't feeding my body, and by doing that I was putting it under stress. But even though I'd been training for years with everyone from the Marist Seniors to the All Blacks, no had actually told me to eat before the game. No one had said, "Have a good meal early on the day of the game, then have something midmorning, even something an hour before the game or at halftime, to replace what you've lost". I didn't understand how the body used food, how to fuel it, how it derived and used energy. I needed the basic information and even though I'd had all these good coaches, no one had thought to tell me.

I finally started eating before games in about 1993, and it made a difference, but even then it was another few years before I really sat down and thought about how I should be managing the food I eat. Basically that happened when I first sat down with Lee and we went through my diet and he explained what I needed to do. It was a revelation. I needed to rearrange the way I ate, eating more meals, less food but more often. We also worked out a few supplements I could use to help.

Getting into a sensible routine was the first thing I had to practise. My eating habits often used to get out of synch with my body clock. Sometimes I'd get up late and eat breakfast at 10 o'clock or 11 o'clock, then of course I wouldn't feel like eating at lunchtime, so I'd have a nibble in the afternoon and end up forcing myself to eat dinner at nine o'clock at night. I

Margot Butcher

It's important to enjoy life and Zinny still enjoys his coffee when he's training - but in moderation.

was really inconsistent that way. Instead I needed to get into good habits, making sure I ate at the right times for training and for my body to get value out of what I was feeding it.

So now I have a pretty good breakfast somewhere between 7 and 8 in the morning, then a nibble mid-morning (and that can be a supplement, like a Powerbar - which is a better thing to do than allow myself to get hungry before lunch and then grab one of those tempting chocolate bars at the service station or dairy. A lot of the supplements that Twinlab provide stop you from feeling nibblish, and at the same time they're fuelling your body properly). Then I'll have a reasonably good lunch, then a snack again mid-afternoon. Then dinner. It helps to have your dinner earlier than say eight in the evening, but that can be hard to coordinate with my lifestyle. I should probably be eating at six or seven o'clock, but sometimes I find myself eating at nine. If I do, I know I can't eat as much - if I eat late I feel as if I've just had Christmas lunch, bloated and uncomfortable. That can interfere with the quality of my rest and carry through into the next day, so I don't do it, even if I'm really hungry.

When I started to put more thought into how and when I ate, I wrote it all down. It's probably like belonging to Weightwatchers: you have to be clinical about it, write down what you're doing to see what's happening, what you're really doing with food.

That doesn't mean that life suddenly gets boring and strict. I'm still flexible. I have my little binges where I have my sweets, if I've been following a programme for two or three months and I just feel like loosening up. You want to reward yourself sometimes and I see nothing wrong with that. If a new ice-cream or chocolate bar's out, I want to try it, although when you get into a pattern of eating good food, when you've disciplined yourself for a while, it actually feels funny when you eat the "wrong" stuff. But if I like having a release from it now and then, I don't think I should feel guilty about it. So every now and then I have my chocolate bar or my *Jelly Tip*, which I like. A few coffees with sugar. But that's kept in perspective. I believe in moderation. I don't suddenly buy a King Size block - I'll buy a little "chunky" bar, and I might try to give some of it away.

Knowing how to eat at the right times has really helped me on the sporting field. It's helped me stay alert on the day of the game, given me energy at the right times. I'm careful now to eat properly three or four days before the game, and especially the day of the game. The night before, I find it's really important to eat the right meal, the right type of fuel. Same with breakfast in the morning - nowadays I like to have spaghetti, baked beans, maybe a couple of boiled eggs, a cup of tea, toast and a bit of fruit - a good breakfast. Then I like having a couple of bananas and a *Twinlab* thickshake before I leave for the ground (or I'll have one at the ground). Then I feel really good. I've loaded up with carbohydrates and I know my energy reserves are there.

When I started down this track, I didn't feel like someone was going to wave a wand over me and transform me, voilà! I wanted to test the theories out. Sometimes in games, I felt really good and sometimes I still felt flat. You have to analyse it yourself, why you felt one way or the other. Was it the way you ate, or something you did the night before the game, did you sleep well? For me, it was trial and error, but I definitely noticed the difference that came from making sure I got the right food and putting the right supplements into my body. It could have been the 'x-factor' for me in some games.

Thinking about your food can be part of your goalsetting. Sit down and ask yourself, how many times do I pick up a chocolate bar when I'm in the gas station paying for $20 of petrol? Identifying little habits like that and correcting them could be the little thing that makes the difference to achieving the body you want.

Nowadays I think about the type of food I'm eating every time it passes my lips. I want to know if something is good for me or not. That doesn't mean fretting that something is perhaps 5% or 10% or more fat: again, it's unrealistic to be too fanatical, in my view. But by understanding what kinds of food you're eating, what the protein, carbohydrate or fat content is, you can guide yourself towards a healthy balance.

In our house we eat really well. It takes a bit of preparation, but it's worth it. We make sure we eat good meals, that the food's fresh and full of nutrients. We cook. We like variety. And we know what we're eating. We've sorted out the tricky foods - like avocado. You wouldn't think avocado would be high in fat, but it is. Same with peanuts, peanut butter, butter - I tend to avoid those. I don't eat much butter, actually. In fact, if I put it on bread it's purely for the visual effect and I spread it real thin over the bread instead of caking it on.

When I lived in Italy for two years, I discovered that the Italians don't eat butter at all. At first it was something I really missed, but I ended up that way myself and it was quite a good move: I've found out I don't need to eat as much as I used to consume. It's just fat, after all.

I find that when I have a break from training or playing, I really have to watch what I eat, because it's easy to eat a lot of food as you normally would do, but you don't burn it off, so you put on weight. So I usually cut back on my meals when I'm in my chill-out phase, although as I said, I still enjoy little treats.

As far as supplements go, taking supplements won't make you an All Black. They're not magic powders. But they will help you when you use them correctly to help fuel, replenish and build your body.

There's quite a few options you can use, but I use Hydrafuel, Ultrafuel and Optifuel 2 (which is like a carboloader) myself, and snack-like Powerbars, Twinlab bars as well. They're basically to stop me bingeing. I carry a few around most times, carry them with me when I pull into that gas station, see the pretty chocolate bars and feel the urge to binge, or go into a dairy and see all the ice-cream. I have a Powerbar instead.

Sometimes a change is good. When I get tired of taking the same supplements all the time I just talk to my nutrition guy and say, "Look, is there anything else I can take that's similar to this stuff?" and he'll work something out. But I always load up with Ultrafuel and Hydrafuel before games and the day of the game.

No one's tested me to prove that supplements have made the difference, and it could be purely psychological. But if it is, it's working. I'm sure the supplements are good, but even so, psychologically there's an effect as well, I think. You feel prepared. You feel you've done everything you need to meet the opposition.

My message is that if you don't know, you've got to ask. Ask a doctor or a dietitian. Before I asked about supplements and nutrition, I didn't know how I could enhance my performance. Then I had to work out what worked for me. Everyone's different, so I'm not suggesting that anyone go out and copy my personal nutrition programme, but you can apply the same principles of thinking about it properly and testing what works for you.

As far as hydration goes, making sure that you get good water intake is just as important as fuelling your body. You can never drink too much water, in my opinion. Justin Marshall, Taine Randell and I used to have competitions to see how much water we could each drink - Justin and I could drink between 10 and 15 bottles each the day of the game. You don't need to be that extreme, but you do need plenty of water. Having a little often is a very good idea.

Another thing I want to mention is alcohol. I'm pretty flexible on this issue and while I could reel off all the reasons not to drink, to be honest I don't avoid it totally. I used to - I never used to drink. When I first came to Auckland as a young guy and played for Marist Seniors, I used to go to the bar and order a raspberry and lemonade, or water or orange juice.

But to me now, socialising and having a beer is part of the New Zealand culture and it's become part of my make-up. People do say that you shouldn't drink beer before the game, because it affects your performance, but most nights before a game I'll have a can of beer. Sometimes I'll have two. That's not uncommon. I've never felt that it's affected my performance. If I was a 100 metre sprinter, I'm sure it would, but I haven't found it the case in rugby. We also drink beer after the game, some of us. It comes down to what you personally feel comfortable with.

But in saying that, how many people drink alcohol on a Friday night or Saturday night, but then don't flush the body the next morning of all the toxins and rubbish that's built up in it as a result? I believe that if you're prepared to drink alcohol, you've got to be prepared to work on the other side of it as well.

If I occasionally have more than a couple of beers, that gives me even more reason to go *and sweat it out. The next day I'll jump on my bike at home for 45 minutes and really go for it, get it out of my system. I'm prepared to do that. You feel awful to begin with, but once you've sweated it out in training with hard yakka, you feel awesome.*

I know that technically, alcohol is not good for sports performance. But again it's finding the balance that works for you. For me, I want to relax and enjoy a beer sometimes, and I also want to keep it in control. If I don't feel like having a beer, I don't. I don't get trapped into drinking just because everyone else is. That used to happen a lot in team sport I think, but as people are getting more aware, that scene is changing.

On the other hand, after the last test in Pretoria in 1996, I actually felt so flat that I decided to bypass having a drink afterwards or going out that evening, and just went back to the hotel room and crashed. I ended up sitting up until three in the morning, watching videos because my mind was still keyed up and turning over the events of the game. In that situation, I actually would have been better off, personally, going out and having a couple of beers to unwind and relax, helping release the stress and tension after a week in which the pressure had been building up inside me. When I feel that way now, I know from experience that it's better for me to go out and have a few beers than not to go out at all.

Of course there's no way I would get my ultimate performance in rugby if I was going over the top drinking beer every week. It's like a cliff: you can have a look over the top, but don't jump off the edge. You can't afford to. And take it from me, as you get older, your body doesn't handle excess well at all. If I were to drink too much on a Saturday night now, I would not recover physically until Tuesday. That could throw out my whole training week. So the key is, get the balance right. Get everything in perspective."

chapter (9)

The Skill Factor

*I*n this book we've mainly discussed knowledge and tips that a sportsperson of any age or experience can use to improve their sports performance. But our final two chapters are dedicated to two very special ingredients that are best developed from a young age, from your first, tentative steps in sporting life: skill and toughness.

FOOLS RUSH IN

No matter what your sport, when you're young, it's important to actually stay *out* of the gym. The focus for kids should never be on heart rates and strength training, on getting physically stronger and fitter, but on fun and enjoyment in sport and learning and practising skills. After all, without mastering the essential skills of a sport, like passing in netball and rugby or playing a good forward defence shot or back foot drive in cricket, you're not going to get very far. Skill is always your most essential ability in sport.

What's more, if you start training and developing your body in a gym when you're still growing, you will do yourself far more harm than good. The real dangers of both damage to posture and potential burnout mean it's just not a smart idea.

So when is it finally OK to walk into a gym for the first time to start training? The answer really depends on the individual, because everyone's body and growth is different. Generally speaking, it's no good bringing a 14-year-old into the gym to try to make him or her stronger. It's still too early in his or her growth phase to do that. Instead he or she should be concentrating on the skill factors of their sport. Then, depending on their physical development, they could look at beginning a strength training programme anywhere from the age of 18, 20 or more - whenever they've left the adolescent phase and their bones have matured. You just can't rush it, and it's important that kids aren't sucked into thinking that training in a gym will help them push into a school first XV or first XI. It's not worth the risk - you don't want to burn them out before they have reached their potential. And there are still lots of other important edges you can gain without taking a risk with your body, such as getting into good nutritional/fuelling habits and ensuring you maximise your recovery after games.

Obviously there's a wide range of physical attributes and speed of physical maturity in any community. For example, a number of Maori and Polynesian kids look like they're born to play contact sport: they tend to grow up quicker, earlier, stronger. But that doesn't mean they should be in the gym any earlier. Why throw them into the gym when they've already got strength at a young age? They should also wait until they're older and have matured.

Photosport: Neil McKenzie

Kicking is a skill Zinny has trained since he was a boy. Here he attempts a drop-goal against Wellington in the 1996 NPC.

Wait for nature, for the hormonal/endocrine system to take its course, and also for the person to have developed things like skill, enjoyment, attitude and discipline. Then, and only then, start to think about training to get even better.

It really is important not to push an athlete in the wrong areas at an early age. Think about it. It's relatively easy to train strength and physical fitness in an athlete, but it's very hard to get an 18 or 20-year-old and try to teach them *skill*. It's something you should really have learned over the years before that age and if you haven't, everyone else will probably have an edge over you.

Zinzan Brooke was renowned as an All Black for his incredible range of skills - he was the player who had it all, who could tackle as well as kick, who could score a try, kick a drop goal, side-step, pass, set up play and run a clever angle to set up his teammate. He had vision.

These are things he practised as a kid, more than a decade before he first stepped into a gym (and even then, he really wasn't too serious about training his body!). He's the *ultimate* sportsperson to talk about the subject of skill, so let's hear what he has to say:

ZINZAN BROOKE:

"When you're younger, I think sport should be all about having fun. Having fun, sliding around in the mud and dirt, getting muddy on a Saturday afternoon, having a glass of Coca-Cola or juice or sipping on the froth of Dad's beer afterwards and simply enjoying life.

I encourage young people to play all kinds of sports - whatever they want to play. Parents should be open-minded and let kids sort out what they like, too. I don't think the reason a kid plays rugby should be because everyone else is playing it or Dad played it or his older brothers played it or he 'ought' to be a good rugby player. Kids should simply have the freedom to have fun playing any sport and as many sports as they want and find out what they really enjoy. After all, you don't really have to make a decision about what sport you particularly want to play, if you want to concentrate on one, until you're older; until you're perhaps 17 or 18, in most cases. Even older. And whatever sport you do take up in the meantime is still going to develop your hand-eye coordination, whether it's cricket, netball, rugby or tennis. It's going to develop basic physical skill, which is the base for all sports.

When I look back, I realise how important that whole process of learning skills was to my later career, even though I didn't realise that I was actually "training" at the time. Grabbing a ball in the house and running out on to the backyard: that's training. Every time a kid looks at a ball, he's training, because he wants to do something with it. He wants to go out with a friend and try to beat his mate. He wants to go outside and throw the ball around with his Dad, he wants to go outside and throw the ball around with his Mum or try to beat his mother round the house. A kid's training field is his house, his backyard and his training partners are his school friends, his brothers and sisters, his family.

When I was younger, I used to model myself on All Black Sid Going. I used to love his wide passes and his reverse passes, so I used to run around the backyard pretending I was him and practising those skills. It was the same with all the other skills we use in rugby. I didn't realise all those days kicking the old ball around the paddock around the pine trees and through all the Totara trees on our farm were developing skills that I would use in a test match when I got older. But whether you grow up to be an All Black or not, there's going to come a time when you're going to be put in a situation in a game where you're going to have to show your skill in an instant, a situation where you have to act on natural instinct - which is actually an instinct that you will have learned and trained over all those years. That's the importance of the skill factor as opposed to the gym.

It's only because I practised all those skills so much when I was younger that when I need to use them now, I don't lack confidence - and confidence is everything in my game. I don't think to myself, "Geez, where's this kick going to go?". Instead I know within myself that I had the ability to do it when I was younger so why shouldn't I be able to do it now?

A classic example is the drop goal I scored against England in the 1995 World Cup. You know, I used to practise that until the cows came home on the farm! That's why I felt I could do it. I still remember Mike Brewer standing in front of me going, "No, Zinny, no!" Screaming at me not to take such a risk. But I was quite calm and relaxed about it. It was an opportunity that seemed quite natural, because I'd practised it. Straight after the game, all those childhood memories came flooding back to me. I thought, 'Yeah, so that's why I practised kicking balls round trees with my brothers!'

Photosport: Joanna Caird

Zinny on the charge against the Springboks in 1997 at Eden Park.

You don't have to train your body in order to be able to practise skills, so I don't think kids should be doing gym work at all. When you're younger, your body's growing, it's changing all the time, your bones are still soft. Don't mess with it.

Some Pacific Island kids seem to develop a lot earlier than say 17 or 18, but other kids can develop and fill out later. But even for those early-maturing Island kids, why do they need to be pushing weights any earlier? They've got a natural advantage anyway. Why rush, and risk mucking up your body? Maybe you are *physically stronger and bigger than the other kids, but haven't actually stopped growing. Remember the big picture. Pushing weights in the gym when you're 16, 17 to try to make yourself bigger for the big first XV clash isn't going to win you much in the long run.*

By pushing weights at too early an age, you can push your body into a different form, and create stresses and bad alignment that will end up causing you a lot of injuries and pain. You only get one body, one set of bones, so look after it and before you start training in the gym, make sure you get expert advice. Don't try to judge yourself whether you're developed enough to start pushing weight. You can't. Don't be hurried or forced into it, and don't think that just because you're mate's pushing weights, you can too. Everyone's different.

The muscle factor is something that can be developed successfully much further down the line, when you're older - but it's a lot harder to train the skill factor if you start when you're older. I know that for a fact, having seen some Spanish, French, Italian and Argentinean rugby players who haven't started playing the game until they've been perhaps 12 or 13: you could see that they had missed out on that grass root, instinctive play. Then I look at some of the kids who run around near my house in Auckland, and I'm amazed at their great level of skill. I never had skills like they do when I was their age - it wasn't until about 1985 that I even started doing grid games, passing the ball behind my back and under my knees.

Before that, I just used to practise the pass. So kids and teenagers now have far more advanced skills. They're a lot better off, and that's enough for them to enjoy playing right through until their body's fully grown. They should be thinking about learning and practising all the basic skills before they start thinking about pushing weight in gyms, because there will come that time when there'll be asked to perform those skills in a moment in a game - and when they pull it off, they'll understand."

chapter **10**

The Toughness Factor

*L*et's face it: some people are tougher than others. They simply exude that never-say-die attitude in sport and in their lives and seem to draw from an invisible pool of determination and self-discipline within themselves. They don't show pain or fatigue as readily as other people, they don't give in as easily as other people, they don't back off as quickly as other people. The mental and emotional aspects of their sports performance operate at an elite level and that, even more than their physical training and optimum nutrition, is what gives them a competitive edge.

But while you might think that when it comes to toughness, some people have it and some people don't, it's probably closer to the mark to say that we *all* have toughness, but in different degrees. What's more, even if you don't have a lot of it, you *can* still train toughness.

You may not get to the same level of toughness as someone who was born with bullets between his teeth, but you can still train yourself to hold yourself up and pull your shoulders back even though you want to lie down because you're so tired. You can use the positive effects of mind-talk by telling yourself, "*I'll become emotionally tough, this is my challenge.*" Because you are a competitor, you will respond to that challenge, and you will become tougher.

Someone who's never rested on their laurels, who has instead developed a habit of challenging themselves, is usually going to have an edge over someone who hasn't - but that someone who hasn't can still change to a degree, for the better, to be different. They will improve, and that mental improvement might be enough to take them into a better team, whether it's from the D team to the C team or the B team to the A team.

Your training environment is where you have the freedom to experiment with toughness. It's where you challenge yourself to go up another level. Some people will freeze, or even stop, go back and retrace their steps when you ask them to achieve something new in training, push to a new level, but the people who are tough seem to find that little bit extra when it's needed, every single time. It's not just a physical thing: it's very much an emotional ability, too. You've got to summon up more determination as well as more energy. You've got to be prepared to give yourself a chance.

If you know that you've been there in training, that you've pushed through limits mentally, set new standards of performance, then you know you can do it on the park or in the pool or on the court. It's about an attitude, willpower, your determination, the talk that you give yourself and particularly the talk you give yourself when you think you want to stop.

Your training environment is the ideal place to experiment with your levels of toughness because if you make a mistake in training, you have the opportunity to say to yourself, or to say to your coach or trainer, "OK, I didn't handle that well, what can I do about it?". Then you can try again.

Because you may not get a second opportunity as easily in an actual game or race situation, you shouldn't leave it until the big day to find out how tough you really are. You can be so much better prepared than that.

In training, realise that failure is not failure. Failure is a learning experience, if you apply yourself to improvement (and neverending improvement is the goal in sport and life). When Sean Fitzpatrick and Zinzan Brooke "fail" to do something in training, that's not a negative experience for them. Their toughness factor ensures they turn the experience into a positive, a tool to ensure they get there next time. When they *do* get there next time, their initial failure has helped them, because they've learned something in the process.

Remember, the environment that you train in is not just where you train yourself physically, but where you train yourself mentally and emotionally.

There is a belief factor in toughness, too. You've got to believe in yourself. We sometimes think of people who exude self-belief as "arrogant", but successful sportspeople and even business people have to have this certain "arrogance", a confidence that they can do what the person next to them possibly can't. It's a healthy, powerful thing to believe in yourself and a state of mind that's going to help you project the right body language to your competitors.

Your mind-talk and your body language tell the story.

ZINZAN BROOKE:

"How do you describe toughness? It's actually a 'tough' question, but I know it's an attitude or a quality that I've always had. It's what I call this 'mongrel streak' in me that means once I bite something, I want to hold on and just not drop it.

It's never changed, that attitude. The only thing that has changed is that when I was young, I didn't understand the need for balance in my life and in my mind - rugby was my life. Now I've recognised the need for balance in that I have a life outside training and rugby and I don't spend every minute of my waking day in sport. But that doesn't affect my toughness. Like everything else you train, toughness is a quality you turn on when you need it.

If you have the competitive edge you'll always push yourself through this certain barrier in training. I notice it especially when I'm training with my brother Rob and Fitzy, for instance: if I go to the gym and see Fitzy training, I'll always go and say to Lee, "What did Fitzy push?" Lee might give me something lighter, but I'll want to push more, because Fitzy can. Then Fitzy will come back the next day and say, "What did Zinny do?".

I've always used my mind-talk when I'm training or playing. It might be as simple as saying to myself, "Come on, come on", or grunting. And I've got no time for negative thoughts. It's something I've cultured over years and it signals a certain response within me. I think everyone's mind-talk is different, but for me, I know what I'm capable of, what my maximum is and how to push myself to get there.

It's a hard thing to explain, the way you "feel" your barrier, but that's what you've got to learn to do. For instance, I find sometimes team training is harder than playing a game, but I know that if I push myself through a barrier in training, I'll know I can do it in the game. The precautions with that approach are that you can push those limits, but you mustn't fatigue yourself or the team in the process, either physically or mentally. Your mind is what pushes the body, so you have to be careful not to mentally fatigue someone. You can fatigue someone's body but the thing that will crack them is the mind.

You should train the way you mean to play. If you know you can push yourself, that you've got a certain toughness that you've shown on the training field, it means that you're going to handle a pressure situation or a personal challenge on the sports field a whole lot better.

A classic example is when I'm playing golf. I always seem to play my best stroke when I'm practising. I free up, loosen up and it just feels good when I swing the club. But then I stick a ball in front of it, I tense up and it just doesn't go right. So the real pressure comes on when I'm just off the green and the other guy's just played up his shot and then I've got to play my shot to be inside his ball. I've noticed that I've often cracked in that situation - topped the ball and knocked it just two metres in front of me - simply because of the pressure. I haven't had the confidence to take hold of the moment.

So what I need to do in golf is to train myself to relax not just when I'm practising, but when I'm playing my actual shots. That's a form of training emotional toughness; your emotional response to a challenge. I've got to develop the x-factor in my game where I have the balls to say to myself that I'm going to have a go at it and I'm going to nail it.

In the rugby sense I don't have that problem at all. I already know there's nothing that I won't try, because I have the confidence and all the skills that I've had since I was a kid. For example, when I was a little guy kicking the ball around, I used to practise kicking all the time. Then, when I first came to Auckland, people used to say to me that "No 8s don't kick". If I'd had a number 12 or 13 on my back it would have been instantly all right, but just because I was a forward... So I used to say, "Why not? It doesn't say that in the rule book". Because I didn't accept that limitation, kicking continued to be a special part of my game. I carried off my drop goals because I had the balls to put my skill on the line after all that practice in the backyard. I backed myself. It was a confidence that came from having trained both my skill and my toughness.

John Eales is another classic example - he's a forward, but he takes line kicks and goal kicks - and he's good. Consciously or subconsciously, you don't want to be stuck in a box.

Mark Smith

Training his mental toughness in golf: the next challenge for Zinzan Brooke.

Again, you need to have trained all those skills so that when you put yourself into a situation where you have to use them, you have both the ability and the guts, the confidence, and the toughness to do it. Just think of a batsman in cricket. In cricket, every ball coming to you is a test of whether you back yourself to hit it or play it well. That's why batsmen are often characterised as arrogant, because they project that sense of backing themselves. This is the kind of thing that actually applies to men and women in any sport, but I don't see anything wrong with projecting your self-belief.

You've got to keep challenging yourself so that you can respond better all the time. You're not going to get anywhere by playing safe time after time. That applies both in the gym when you need to push yourself, and in, say, a team training situation where you're going to get more out of yourself by having the confidence to use your imagination and try different things. When I have a team training, I don't want guys to come along and be sheep. I want them to show me this new move off the back of the scrum. I want them to think outside the square and have the confidence to pull it off.

Toughness to me isn't an aggressive, over-the-top attitude. And some people are physically tough, but they might not be emotionally tough or mentally tough. Some people have it all, but others are mentally babies. They can go and smash someone, but if they get smashed, they back down.

I think toughness is really a mindset where you react in a game situation without even having to think about it, question it. I believe you've simply always got to have a go at something, and that could be the x-factor in your game. That's what it is, and that's something you may have naturally, or you may have in part and then train over time. If you're not prepared to believe in yourself and have a go, you may as well pack your bags and go home.

I think that there is still a fine line between toughness and stupidity - they're like different faces of stubbornness. Coming through an injury is when you need toughness, for example, but if you're not looking after your body properly, it can also be where you blow it by being too stubborn.

A classic example (of my stupidity as much as anything) is when I was trying to pass a fitness test to go to the 1995 World Cup. I had injured my leg (my Achilles tendon was torn) and had gone on an intensive rehab programme for five weeks to get it right. It was very hard training - lots of water-running - and I didn't want it all to be for nothing. I really wanted to be on the plane flying to the World Cup in South Africa.

To prove my fitness, I had to run 800 metres, twice around an athletics track, in front of All Black selectors and medical staff. It sounds like nothing, but when you've got a sore Achilles, it's murder!

When I arrived, I spent 15 minutes warming up the Achilles, because there was no way I could have jumped out of the car and then run. So I really stretched it out, and then began, with Peter White (he was North Harbour's fitness trainer) running alongside me for support.

All I had to do was jog around the track and I would go to the World Cup. It was a real slow jog, but that didn't matter. I just had to prove I could go the distance. But after just 100 metres, I was in so much discomfort I thought, 'Geez, I'm not going to make it here.' In my warm-up, I'd jogged about 20 metres, but then I'd stop and stretch, jog, then stop and stretch again. This was the first time I'd actually run further. I looked across at Whitey and he said, "You guts it out, you go through that wall".

I said, "I can't mate, I'm knackered" - which was very unlike me. But I did decide that I had to guts it out, and when I got to 600 metres to go I decided I had to try to run normally. I was gritting my teeth. The pain was excruciating, but I was trying to mask it.

I got to 500 to go and thought then that I was out of the World Cup. With 400 to go I can remember saying to Whitey, "The World Cup, it's gone". But he said to me, "Keep going".

I got around to within 300 metres of the target and by 200 I was literally just hopping along. I would have been doing 30 seconds per hundred metres!

Then Whitey said, "You've got 100 metres to go and you're going to the World Cup". I started striding out a bit more, doubling the pace. I wasn't going to give in. And I made it.

Brian Lochore and the doctors and physio walked up to me and said, "Yep, you're going to the World Cup". I just walked away and couldn't believe I'd done it. When I ran that first 100 metres, I'd thought I'd never get there. It was the hardest 800 metres I've ever done in my life - and to get through it was pure mental toughness. If you've never experienced that, pushing through trauma, it's hard to explain it. But it was an amazing sensation. I felt I could do anything.

Having said that, I still want to say that it's really important that you listen to your body and be sensible when something isn't right.

I did finally learn that lesson myself. In 1997, for the first time in my career, I said "No." I decided to hang back and miss two Super 12 games at the start of the season because I knew inside that I wasn't ready, I wasn't physically right. Looking back, it's probably the best thing I did, setting me up for a great year. I did get pressured to play those games - and the more people who tell you that you're OK to play, the more you feel you should. It's amazing how you get yourself in the situation. But I exercised a "smart toughness" and stood up for myself. I showed my maturity.

Players in that situation almost need to isolate themselves and say, "Look, what is good for me here?" It certainly wouldn't have been good for me to have had cortisone injections in my injured groin just so I could have played two games when my body wasn't ready for it. I was trying to be honest with myself. I always knew there was pressure on me, and that there would be pressure on me to come back and that I'd have to come back, but I accepted that challenge.

Another example of that kind of mental toughness (maturity) was John Kirwan in Argentina in 1991. He made a decision not to play in a test match because of an injured hamstring - and gave John Timu his test debut, his big chance. Players have this thing about never giving other people opportunities, but you've got to be sensible about it, make sure it's not to the detriment of yourself. Parents and coaches have to take that on board too - and kids should never let themselves be pushed around by a coach or parent who's just thinking of their own glory.

I'm not one of these guys who stand in the weights room making Tarzan noises - that's not toughness. I just want to be good, that's what drives me. You just want to be the best. You do ask yourself why do you push yourself through all that bloody pain in training? Why do you do it? Why do you wake up week in and week out and push yourself through that barrier? I'm asking myself that question now and I still don't really know. It's a competitive streak in certain people that makes them good or makes them go, makes them want that. Makes them not satisfied with just being ordinary. It's just that competitive edge, probably.

You only get one shot at the title in your life, I guess. For me, my title time was from when I first started playing provincial rugby to when I finished playing for the All Blacks. There's no coming back when you've been through that period of your life, so you want to make the most of it. I've been lucky. I've had 11 years at the top, 11 with the All Blacks and 12 with Auckland. That's a huge amount of time to be involved with the All Blacks, but over my lifespan, it's probably not going to be a large percentage of my life. I feel lucky and privileged to have been there, but I also know that training smart helped me make the most of those special times in my life."

The Last Word

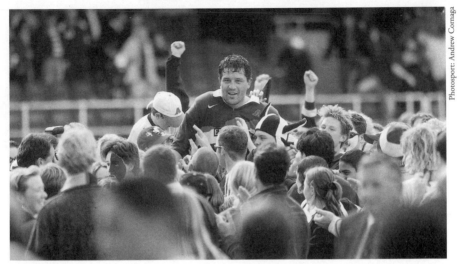

Photosport: Andrew Cornaga

*T*his is what it's all about. Moments when all the experience, effort and knowledge you have put together in training turns into the enjoyment you give to other people and the pleasure you get from knowing you've given your best on the sports field.

I guess my parting message is that hard yakka means hard yakka and there's no getting away from it in training. You do have to reach inside of yourself and push yourself and sweat hard sometimes – and no one can teach you to do that but yourself. You need to have that drive and desire. But if, at the same time, you can train smart and use your head to look after your body, and make some changes where they're needed, you're making a smart move. It's an investment in yourself and your future.

Training with Lee Parore for the last three and a half years has been a great experience for me both as a sportsperson and an individual trying to make the most out of myself. I've learned a lot about motivation, planning my goals, understanding and feeling my body, good nutrition, and the importance of getting and keeping balance and perspective in my life, to name just a few points that we've covered in this book. It's been tremendously satisfying learning to do these things properly and getting more out of myself as a person and a player as a result.

I hope that we have given you an insight into how you can now achieve your goals and make the most of yourself. I wish you luck and enjoyment as you go to meet your own personal challenge. All the best,